Springboards
5

Jaap Tuinman

CONSULTANTS
Sharon Anderson
Elaine Baker
John Drysdale
Julie Kniskern
Joanne McCabe
Claudia Mitchell
Maureen Neuman
Sharon Rich
Kathleen Rosborough

PROGRAM EDITOR
Kathleen Doyle

Ginn and Company
Educational Publishers

Journeys
SPRINGBOARDS
5

EDITORS
Christel Kleitsch
Kathleen O'Connor

Editorial Consultant
Nicki Scrimger

ART/DESIGN
Sandi Meland Cherun/Word & Image Design Studio

C97590
ISBN 0-7702-1214-X

Printed and bound in Canada.
CDEFG   089098

Table of Contents

Bits, Bytes, Chips, and Blips 83

On Stage, Please 105

Dreamers and Doers 123

Love That Book! 145

Getting Together

Because we do
All things together
All things improve,
Even weather.

Our daily meat
And bread taste better,
Trees are greener,
Rain is wetter.

— by Paul Engle

HOME

Oh, Joyous House

by Richard Janzen, 12

When I walk home from school,
I see many houses
Many houses down many streets.
They are warm, comfortable houses
But other people's houses
I pass without much notice.

Then as I walk farther, farther
I see a house, the house.
It springs up with a jerk
That speeds my pace; I lurch forward.
Longing makes me happy, I bubble inside.
It's my house.

A Family Affair

by Patricia Hancock

"She bonked me once."
"He bonked me back."
"Now my arm will be blue and black."

"He's on my half."
"She hogs the couch."
"You're just as bad as a grizzly grouch."

"That's my ball."
"Well, that's my bat."
"I hope you grow up big and fat."

"To your room!"
"Don't do that, Mother."
"She's my sister." "He's my brother."

IS...

A Gang at Supper Time

by Bernice Thurman Hunter

I could hardly wait to see Josie again. Of all the ten kids in our family, I think I missed her the most. And we were closest in age. She was twelve years old and I was thirteen. Actually, there was one month in the year when we were both the same age (April), so we had been raised together like twins.

We shared everything: baths and bicycles, slingshots and skipping ropes. We even switched plates at the dinner table sometimes when Ma made something one of us didn't like. You could do that in a big family and nobody would even notice because of the hubbub.

It was this sort of racket at supper time that drove poor Pa to wolf down his meal and make a beeline for his sanctuary in the cellar. He was a quiet man by nature, and Ma often said with a sigh that he wasn't cut out to be the father of such a gang.

from Margaret in the Middle

Today Is Saturday

by Zilpha Keatley Snyder

We started early, just as soon
As Doug had cleaned his room
And Ben had finished with his paper route.
We went the back way up to Walnut Street
And waited on the lawn 'til Mark came out.

And Mark had lots of money—birthday loot—
And he's the kind that likes to shoot the
    works,
And give his friends a treat.

So we went down to Gray's for Cheezy Chips
And pickles, and we sat outside along the curb
    to eat.
We finished up with ice cream—double dips,
With different flavors so we all could taste around.
And what we couldn't eat we gave to Jake,
That big old mutt who kind of lives down town.
We sat there on the curb and talked awhile,
About the kind of things that we might do.
But Mark had lost his softball, and for once
We didn't feel like fishing in the slough.

So we just wandered off along the path
That starts behind the school, without a plan.
We really still weren't going anywhere,
But when we felt like running, we just ran.

The day was like that—and the things we did
Just happened. And someway, that made them seem
More special than the things we mostly do,
A little bit like something from a dream,
I guess. It was an ordinary day.
Not cloudy, but the sun was kind of dusty gold,
And never very hot.

But everything we did was fun—and no one fought
For once. We laughed a lot
At things nobody else might even see.

No one would know what it was like I guess,
But guys like Doug and Ben and Mark and me.

The Hackers Club

by Arthur Packard

SIMI: Hey Georgie! I didn't know your house had an attic.

GEORGIE: Don't you think this would be a perfect place for our computer club?

ED: But will your parents let us use it?

GEORGIE: They said we can have the whole attic to ourselves if we fix it up, and clean it up.

SIMI: Whew! That's going to be a big job.

ED: It has to be pretty dust-free if we're going to set up my computer in it.

GEORGIE: Well, does anybody have a better suggestion for a clubhouse? I mean it's dry, and it's private. Nobody's going to bother us here . . .

SIMI: And we do have our own entrance up those back stairs.

ED: I guess we could put shelves along this side . . .

GEORGIE: And a desk over here.

SIMI: Okay! Let's get to work.

(Many days, and much elbow grease later)

GEORGIE: It looks great. Just one last thing—a sign on the door. What should it say? "Private Club—Keep Out"?

ED: How about—"Hackers Hideaway."

SIMI: Ed, you're a genius. Paint it, Georgie.

GEORGIE: How do you spell "hideaway"? Two words, or one?

ED: One word. And don't forget the "Keep Out."

SIMI: Who are we going to keep out?

ED: Everybody except the members—that's you, me, Georgie, and my little brother Frank when I have to look after him.

GEORGIE: Don't we want any new members?

SIMI: How about Janice Ashe. She's pretty good on computers, and she has lots of ideas. And how about Tony and Teresa?

ED: Hey. How big do we want this club to get? If we have too many people none of us will get any time on the computer.

GEORGIE: But three members doesn't sound like enough. It doesn't seem like a real club, with just us.

SIMI: And we could schedule time so everybody got a fair share.

GEORGIE: But we don't want the whole neighborhood in on this. Five or six kids is enough.

ED: And no airheads.

SIMI: Of course not. We want people with good ideas.

ED: But what kind of ideas? We haven't decided what we're going to do yet.

GEORGIE: Well, it's a computer club.

ED: So?

SIMI: He's right, Georgie. We've got to do something in our club besides just sit around and talk about it.

ED: And we've got to have rules too.

SIMI: Well, each member should know something about computers.

ED: And all the members should own their own computer.

SIMI: No, that's not fair. I don't have a computer.

GEORGIE: Okay. Then each member should have a computer project to do.

ED: Hey, that sounds great. I've got something I want to do.

GEORGIE: What is it?

ED: Well, last year, when we lost Caesar, nobody could remember what his dog licence number was. So why don't we keep a record of everybody's pet licence numbers.

SIMI: That's a terrific idea! We could even print out a card to give to each pet owner in the neighborhood.

GEORGIE: And we can even charge a small fee so we can raise money for our club.

SIMI: Here's another good idea. We could help Gino and Marcia set up this year's floor hockey schedule.

ED: They'd love that. It's usually so hard to keep track of all the players and which team they're on.

SIMI: And if there are any changes in the teams . . .

GEORGIE: Which always happens . . .

SIMI: Our computer could keep track of it in a snap.

ED: The first thing we have to do is print a poster of our club rules.

GEORGIE: Oh, you and your rules.

SIMI: Let's call them something else.

GEORGIE: How about the Hackers Club Code?

ED: Okay. One rule should be "No eating popcorn and chocolate bars near the computer."

SIMI: Or "Never reveal our computer's secret access word."

GEORGIE: Wait a minute. What is our secret access word?

SIMI: How about GES, for Georgie, Ed, and Simi.

GEORGIE: One last rule. Don't let Caesar chew on the diskettes.

ED: Okay, enough talking. Let's get started on a project. Plug in the computer.

SIMI: Where? I don't see any outlets.

GEORGIE: No outlets? How could I forget the most important thing we need for a computer clubhouse!

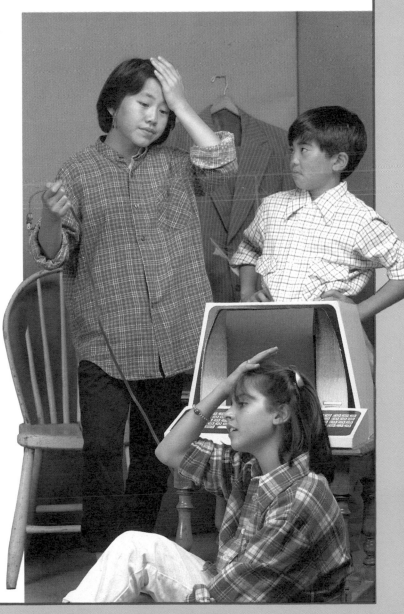

Ramona to the Rescue

by Beverly Cleary

"Cigarettes can kill you. Your lungs will turn black and you'll die!" When Ramona Quimby heard her sister, Beezus, say these words to their father she began worrying about him. She worried in her bed at night and she worried at school the next day. Then suddenly she knew what she had to do.

Ramona made up her mind, right then and there in the middle of arithmetic, that she was going to save her father's life.

That afternoon after school Ramona gathered up her crayons and papers from the kitchen table, took them into her room, and shut the door. She got down on her hands and knees and went to work on the bedroom floor, printing a sign in big letters. Unfortunately, she did not plan ahead and soon reached the edge of the paper. She could not find the Scotch tape to fasten two pieces of paper together, so she had to continue on another line. When she finished, her sign read:

NO SMO KING

It would do. Ramona found a pin and fastened her sign to the living-room curtains,

where her father could not miss it. Then she waited, frightened by her daring.

Mr. Quimby, although he must have seen the sign, said nothing until after dinner when he had finished his pumpkin pie. He asked for an ashtray and then inquired, "Say, who is this Mr. King?"

"What Mr. King?" asked Ramona, walking into his trap.

"Nosmo King," answered her father without cracking a smile.

Chagrined, Ramona tore down her sign, crumpled it, threw it into the fireplace, and stalked out of the room, resolving to do better the next time.

The next day after school Ramona found the Scotch tape and disappeared into her room to continue work on her plan to save her father's life. While she was working, she heard the phone ring and waited, tense, as the whole family now waited whenever the telephone rang. She heard her father clear his throat before he answered. "Hello?" After a pause he said, "Just a minute, Howie, I'll call her." There was disappointment in his voice.

from Ramona and Her Father

No one was calling to offer him a job after all.

"Ramona, can you come over and play?" Howie asked, when Ramona went to the telephone.

Ramona considered. Of course they would have to put up with Howie's messy little sister, Willa Jean, but she and Howie would have fun building things if they could think of something to build. Yes, she would like to play with Howie, but saving her father's life was more important. "No, thank you. Not today," she said. "I have important work to do."

Just before dinner she taped to the refrigerator door a picture of a cigarette so long she had to fasten three pieces of paper together to draw it. After drawing the cigarette, she had crossed it out with a big black X and under it she had printed in big letters the word *BAD*. Beezus giggled when she saw it, and Mrs. Quimby smiled as if she were trying not to smile. Ramona was filled with fresh courage. She had allies. Her father had better watch out.

When Mr. Quimby saw the picture, he stopped and looked while Ramona waited. "Hmm," he said, backing away for a better view. "An excellent likeness. The artist shows talent." And that was all he said.

Ramona felt let down, although she was not sure what she had expected. Anger, perhaps? Punishment? A promise to give up smoking?

The next morning the sign was gone, and that afternoon Ramona had to wait until Beezus came home from school to ask, "How do you spell *pollution?*" When Beezus printed it out on a piece of paper, Ramona went to work making a sign that said, *Stop Air Pollution.*

"Let me help," said Beezus, and the two girls, kneeling on the floor, printed a dozen signs. *Smoking Stinks. Cigarettes Start Forest Fires. Smoking Is Hazardous to Your Health.* Ramona learned new words that afternoon.

Fortunately Mr. Quimby went out to examine the car, which was still making the *tappety-tappety* noise. This gave the girls a chance to tape the signs to the mantle, the refrigerator, the dining-room curtains, the door of the hall closet, and every other conspicuous place they could think of.

This time Mr. Quimby simply ignored the signs. Ramona and Beezus might as well have saved themselves a lot of work for all he seemed to notice. But how could he miss so many signs? He must be pretending. He had to be pretending. Obviously the girls would have to step up their campaign. By now they were running out of big pieces of paper, and they knew better than to ask their parents to buy more, not when the family was so short of money.

"We can make little signs on scraps of paper," said Ramona, and that was what they did. Together they made tiny signs that said, *No Smoking, Stop Air Pollution, Smoking Is Bad for Your Health,* and *Stamp Out Cigarettes.* On some Ramona drew stick figures of people stretched out flat and dead, and on one, a cat on his back with his feet in the air. These they hid wherever their father was sure to find them—in his bathrobe pocket, fastened around the handle of his toothbrush with a rubber band, inside his shoes, under his electric razor.

Then they waited. And waited. Mr. Quimby said nothing while he continued to smoke. Ramona held her nose whenever she saw her father with a cigarette. He appeared not to notice. The girls felt discouraged and let down.

Once more Ramona and Beezus devised a

plan, the most daring plan of all because they had to get hold of their father's cigarettes just before dinner. Fortunately he had tinkered with the car, still trying to find the reason for the *tappety-tappety-tap,* and had to take a shower before dinner, which gave the girls barely enough time to carry out their plan.

All through dinner the girls exchanged excited glances, and by the time her father asked her to fetch an ashtray, Ramona could hardly sit still she was so excited.

As usual her father pulled his cigarettes out of his shirt pocket. As usual he tapped the package against his hand, and as usual a cigarette, or what appeared to be a cigarette, slid out. Mr. Quimby must have sensed that what he thought was a cigarette was lighter than it should be, because he paused to look at it. While Ramona held her breath, he frowned, looked more closely, unrolled the paper, and discovered it was a tiny sign that said, *Smoking Is Bad!* Without a word, he crumpled it and pulled out another—he

thought—cigarette, which turned out to be a sign saying, *Stamp Out Cigarettes!* Mr. Quimby crumpled it and tossed it onto the table along with the first sign.

"Ramona." Mr. Quimby's voice was stern. "My grandmother used to say, 'First time is funny, second time is silly—' " Mr. Quimby's grandmother's wisdom was interrupted by a fit of coughing.

Ramona was frightened. Maybe her father's lungs already had begun to turn black.

Beezus looked triumphant. See, we told you smoking was bad for you, she was clearly thinking.

Mrs. Quimby looked both amused and concerned.

Mr. Quimby looked embarrassed, pounded himself on the chest with his fist, took a sip of coffee, and said, "Something must have caught in my throat." When his family remained silent, he said, "All right, Ramona. As I was saying, enough is enough."

IF I COULD PUT
the WORLD right

Alli Marshall, 10, Yellowknife, N.W.T.

Dear World,

How I'd put the World Right.

I would have all parents hug and kiss their kids while tucking them into bed at night. Then all the boys and girls would grow up with love in their hearts instead of hate and this would bring about peace all over the world cause children don't like to fight.

Love,
Lisa Green

P.S. I still love being tucked in my bed at night.

by Lisa Marie Green, 12, Labrador City, Nfld.

If every brother loved his sister,
What a happy family that would be.

If every family respected its neighbor,
What a friendly community that would be.

If every community worked together,
What a prosperous city that would be.

If every city helped another,
What a strong country that would be.

If every country lived in peace,
What a great world that would be.

by Laura Plant, 12, Toronto, Ont.

I would put the soldiers on farms
They grow crops.
The crops would feed the people.
The guns would make good fence posts.

by Colin Mack, 7, Meota, Sask.

Kristin Kan, grade 6, Nanaimo, B.C.

The good thing about our world is kindness.
The bad thing about our world is cruelty.
The good thing about our world is love.
The bad thing about our world is hatred.
The good thing about our world is peace.
The bad thing about our world is war.
The good thing about our world is health.
The bad thing about our world is sickness.
The good thing about our world is sharing.
The bad thing about our world is greed.
The good thing about our world is happiness.
The bad thing about our world is sadness.
The good thing about our world is comfort.
The bad thing about our world is poverty.
The good thing about our world is generosity.
The bad thing about our world is selfishness.
The good thing about our world is beauty.
The bad thing about our world is ugliness.
The good thing about our world is honesty.
The bad thing about our world is dishonesty.

The good thing about our world is friendship.
The bad thing about our world is enemies.
The good thing about our world is education.
The bad thing about our world is ignorance.
But the best thing about our world is—
People everywhere sharing and caring!

If we only had the power
We'd make the world like a fresh spring flower
We'd keep the good things, and throw out the bad,
So our world would be happy and not so sad.
Cheerful, peaceful, kind, and bright;
Then our world would be just right!

by the grade 4 class, Mill Creek Elementary School, N.S.

Tasha Riley, grade 6, London, Ont.

Inside Out

by Dagmar Guarino

I live in a crowded house.

One day, I wanted something in that house, so I went outside to get it.

I sat down on the front porch and waited. I'm a very patient person, as well as being very intelligent. I knew that, soon enough, I would get just what I wanted.

In a few minutes, my two kid brothers came out of the crowded house and sat on the porch beside me. They are twins, and they make twice as much of a crowd as anyone else in the family.

"Hey, Maggie, what are you doing out here?" asked Robin.

"Yeah, what?" asked Robert.

I took off my glasses and polished them. "I am looking for something inside the house," I said quietly.

"Then why are you sitting out *here*?" asked both the boys.

"Because."

The two boys looked at one another. They know me, and they know what "because" means when I say it. They decided to play things my way.

"Can we try to guess what you want in the house?" Robert asked this time.

I am a reasonable person. "Sure," I said, putting on my glasses again.

So the twins started to guess.

Was it a book? No. A kite? No. The dog? No. Was it animal, vegetable, or mineral? No, no, no.

The twins gave up. Robert thought it would be wise to get some help. He went up to the front door and hollered, "Becky!"

Becky is our older sister. She's fourteen and wears curlers a lot. When she came to the door, she was winding one up in her hair.

"What's the matter?" she asked.

"Come out here and help us guess what Maggie's looking for," said Robin.

Becky finished rolling up her hair, shrugged her shoulders, and sat down on the porch with everyone else. Now the porch was getting crowded. Becky's curlers alone took up a lot of space.

"Okay," she started. "Is it animal, vegetable, or mineral?"

"We already *asked* that!" yelled both the boys at the same time. Being twins, they did that a lot.

"Okay, okay, give me a chance," Becky said quickly. "Hmm . . . is it bigger than a bread box?"

"No," I said very seriously, trying to hide a giggle.

Becky tried some more questions. Did it hop? Could it sing? Did it wear tennis shoes?

I said no to everything.

Finally Becky gave up too. She went to the door and called, "Hey, Mom!"

Our mother came outside with paint on her hands. She likes to do still lifes, and her oil paints are forever crowding up the house.

"What is it?" she asked.

"Would you help us try to guess what Maggie wants in the house," Becky said.

"Okay," said Mom, as she squeezed into a spot near one end of the porch.

"Is it round?"

"No."

"Square?"

"No."

"Could I paint it?"

"I don't think so," I said smugly.

My mother frowned for a moment. Finally she went to the door and said, "This is all very interesting. Let's give your father a chance at it. Peter!"

Then Dad came running out from the kitchen, a finger to his lips. He was always baking things, and his fattening desserts didn't help to thin out the crowded conditions much.

"*Ssh,* not so loud," he said. "I've got cake in the oven."

"Hey, Dad, try and guess what Maggie wants in the house," said Robin.

"My cake?" asked Father, settling down on the opposite end of the porch. He was disappointed when I said no. Usually I just love his cakes.

He tried other things. Bananas? Ice cream? Root beer?

But no, it wasn't any of these things.

"Well, I give up," my father said, looking across the crowd of children at our dog, who was pretty good herself at crowding up the house with chewed-up slippers. She climbed up on Becky's knee and went to sleep. The rest of the family just sat on the porch of the empty house, staring at me and thinking.

At last I squeezed myself out of the crowd and stood up. I guess I must have looked pretty pleased with myself.

"Do all of you really want to know what I wanted inside the house?" I asked, opening the front door.

"Yes!" shouted the whole family, turning to look at me. "What did you want?"

21

"*PRIVACY!*" I said as I stepped inside
the empty house and locked the door.
"Privacy!" I repeated—and I laughed.
   And for the first time ever, I got some.

The Clever and the Foolish

"Rabbit's clever," said Pooh thoughtfully.
"Yes," said Piglet, "Rabbit's clever."
"And he has Brain."
"Yes," said Piglet, "Rabbit has Brain."
There was a long silence.
"I suppose," said Pooh, "that that's why he never understands anything."

— *from* The House at Pooh Corner
by A.A. Milne

The Greedy Butchers

by Ian Serraillier

Come to me, all you young gallants, O come
    From town and meadow and wood!
If you listen a while, I'll sing you a song
    Of an archer, bold Robin Hood.

Once, as he walked in the merry greenwood,
    It chanced bold Robin did see
A butcher astride a bonny fine mare,
    And riding to market was he.

"Good morrow, good fellow," said Robin Hood.
    "What carry you there in your pack?
And tell me your trade and where you dwell—
    I trust you'll safely get back."

The butcher he answered Robin Hood,
    "What matters it where I dwell?
For a butcher am I, and to Nottingham town
    I am going, my meat to sell."

"What is the price of your mare?" said Robin.
    "Tell me, I'm eager to learn.
And what is the price of your meat, for I wish
    As a butcher my living to earn?"

"The price of my meat?" the butcher replied.
    "I can reckon that up in a minute . . .
Four shillings, good sir, is none too dear—
    And a bonny fine mare to go with it."

"Four guineas I'll give you," said Robin Hood,
  "Four guineas in gold I'll pay."
They counted their money, exchanged their clothes,
  And each rode off on his way.

So Robin Hood rode to Nottingham town
  On the butcher's bonny fine mare.
Though others might charge too dear for their meat,
  He vowed *his* price should be fair.

But the sheriff he was in league with these rogues,
  He too was a twister and cheat.
What cared he if the price was too high
  And the poor could buy no meat?

In their stalls the butchers opened their meat,
  On dish and platter displayed;
For many a year they'd swindled the poor,
  But Robin was new to the trade.

Yet not a bite, not a morsel they sold,
  While bountiful Robin did well:
He sold more meat for one penny piece
  Than the rest for three pennies could sell.

Those villainous butchers fell back, amazed;
  The sheriff he scratched his head.
"If this fellow continues in trade, we'll starve.
  We must teach him a lesson," they said.

The butchers stepped over to Robin, resolved
  That some pretty trick should be played.
"Good brother," said one, "will you join us for dinner?
  Do come—we are all in the trade."

"Such offers," said Robin, "I never refuse."
    And to dinner they hurried apace.
The sheriff sat down at the head of the table,
    And asked Robin Hood to say grace.

"And when you've said grace, you shall sit at my side
    And we'll drink to success and long life."
"I'll gladly say grace," said bold Robin Hood,
    "If I may sit next to your wife."

The sheriff agreed. "God bless us!" said Robin.
    "Good appetite! Drink your fill!
Though five pounds and more it cost me in gold,
    I vow that I'll settle the bill."

"This fellow is crazy," the butchers declared.
    Said the sheriff, "He's due for a fall.
He has sold all his land for silver and gold,
    And means to squander it all."

"May he squander it all in this house," said the butchers,
    "And part with it, quick as can be!"
"Be patient! I've thought of a trick," said the sheriff.
    "I beg you to leave it to me."

Said the sheriff to Robin, "What have you to sell?
    Any cattle or hornéd beast?"
"Indeed, I have plenty, good master sheriff,
    Two or three hundred at least."

The sheriff saddled his dapple-gray,
    With three hundred pound in gold;
And away he went with bold Robin Hood,
    His hornéd beasts to behold.

By hill and furrow and field they rode,
    To the forest of merry Sherwood.
"O, Heaven forbid," the sheriff exclaimed,
    "That we meet with Robin Hood!"

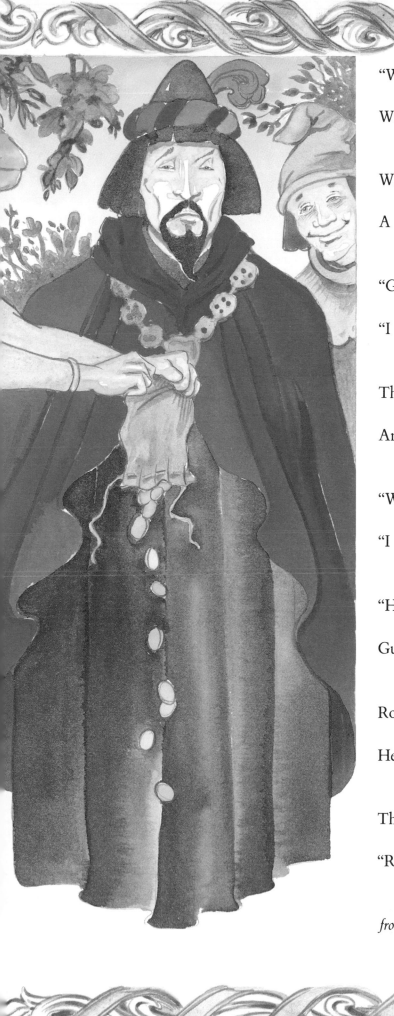

"Why do you tremble and shake?" said Robin.
    "You should trust, good sir, in me.
With my brave longbow and arrows I'll show
    I can shoot as straight as he."

When to a leafy hollow they came,
    Bold Robin chanced to spy
A hundred head of good red deer
    Through the trees come tripping by.

"Good master sheriff, how like you my beasts?
    They're sleek—and see how they race!"
"I tell you, good fellow, I'd rather go home—
    I don't like the look on your face."

Then Robin Hood put his horn to his mouth,
    He blew blasts two and three—
And fifty bowmen with brave Little John
    Stood under the greenwood tree.

"What is your will?" then said Little John.
    "Good master, what must we do?"
"I have brought the sheriff of Nottingham town
    Today to have dinner with you."

"He is welcome indeed," said Little John.
    "I hope from his purse he will pay
Guineas and shillings to give to the poor,
    To gladden them many a day."

Robin Hood stripped the cloak from his back
    And, laying it down on the ground,
He emptied the purse—in silver and gold
    He counted three hundred pound.

Then lo! through the greenwood the sheriff he led,
    Sitting glum on his old dapple-gray.
"Remember me, sir, to your lady at home!"
    Laughed Robin, and galloped away.

from Robin in the Greenwood

Tales of Foolishness

How the Peasant Helped His Horse

retold by Mirra Ginsburg

A peasant drove to market to sell his grain. The roads were bad, and his horse got tired pulling the heavy load. The peasant saw that the horse could not go much farther. He took one of the bags of grain from the cart, put it across his shoulders, climbed back into the driver's seat, and said to the horse, "Giddy-up, giddy-up! It's easier for you now! I am carrying a whole bag on my own shoulders!"

Three Rolls and One Doughnut

retold by Mirra Ginsburg

A peasant walked a long way from his village to the city. By the time he got there, he was very hungry. He bought a roll and ate it, but he was still hungry. He bought another roll and ate it, but he was still hungry. He bought a third roll and ate it. He was still hungry. Then he bought a doughnut. He ate it—and what do you think?—he was not hungry any more.

"Ah!" He clapped himself on the forehead. "What a fool I was to have wasted all that good money on rolls! I should have bought a doughnut to begin with!"

The Snow in Chelm

retold by Isaac Bashevis Singer

Chelm was a village of fools, fools young and old. One night someone spied the moon reflected in a barrel of water. The people of Chelm imagined it had fallen in. They sealed the barrel so that the moon would not escape. When the barrel was opened in the morning and the moon wasn't there, the villagers decided it had been stolen. They sent for the police, and when the thief couldn't be found, the fools of Chelm cried and moaned.

Of all the fools of Chelm, the most famous were its seven Elders. Because they were the village's oldest and greatest fools, they ruled in Chelm. They had white beards and high foreheads from too much thinking.

Once, on a Hanukkah night, the snow fell all evening. It covered all of Chelm like a silver tablecloth. The moon shone; the stars twinkled; the snow shimmered like pearls and diamonds.

That evening the seven Elders were sitting and pondering, wrinkling their foreheads. The village was in need of money, and they did not know where to get it. Suddenly the oldest of them all, Gronam the Great Fool, exclaimed, "The snow is silver!"

"I see pearls in the snow!" another shouted.

"And I see diamonds!" a third called out.

It became clear to the Elders of Chelm that a treasure had fallen from the sky.

But soon they began to worry. The people of Chelm liked to go walking, and they would most certainly trample the treasure. What was to be done? Silly Tudras had an idea.

"Let's send a messenger to knock on all the windows and let the people know that they must remain in their houses until all the sil-ver, all the pearls, and all the diamonds are safely gathered up."

For a while the Elders were satisfied. They rubbed their hands in approval of the clever idea. But then Dopey Lekisch called out in consternation, "The messenger himself will trample the treasure."

The Elders realized that Lekisch was right, and again they wrinkled their high foreheads in an effort to solve the problem.

"I've got it!" exclaimed Shmerel the Ox.

"Tell us, tell us," pleaded the Elders.

"The messenger must not go on foot. He must be carried on a table so that his feet will not tread on the precious snow."

Everybody was delighted with Shmerel the

Ox's solution; and the Elders, clapping their hands, admired their own wisdom.

The Elders immediately sent to the kitchen for Gimpel the errand boy and stood him on a table. Now who was going to carry the table? It was lucky that in the kitchen there were Treitle the cook, Berel the potato peeler, Yukel the salad mixer, and Yontel, who was in charge of the community goat. All four were ordered to lift up the table on which Gimpel stood. Each one took hold of a leg. On top stood Gimpel, grasping a wooden hammer with which to tap on the villagers' windows. Off they went.

At each window Gimpel knocked with the hammer and called out, "No one leaves the house tonight. A treasure has fallen from the sky, and it is forbidden to step on it."

The people of Chelm obeyed the Elders and remained in their houses all night. Meanwhile the Elders themselves sat up trying to figure out how to make the best use of the treasure once it had been gathered up.

Silly Tudras proposed that they sell it and buy a goose which lays golden eggs. Thus the community would be provided with a steady income.

Dopey Lekisch had another idea. Why not buy eyeglasses that make things look bigger for all the inhabitants of Chelm? Then the houses, the streets, the stores would all look bigger, and of course if Chelm *looked* bigger, then it *would be* bigger. It would no longer be a village, but a big city.

There were other, equally clever ideas. But while the Elders were weighing their various plans, morning came and the sun rose. They looked out of the window, and, alas, they saw the snow had been trampled. The heavy boots of the table carriers had destroyed the treasure.

The Elders of Chelm clutched at their white beards and admitted to one another that they had made a mistake. Perhaps, they reasoned, four others should have carried the four men who had carried the table that held Gimpel the errand boy?

After long deliberations the Elders decided that if next Hanukkah a treasure would again fall down from the sky, that is exactly what they would do.

Although the villagers remained without a treasure, they were full of hope for the next year and praised their Elders, who they knew could always be counted on to find a way, no matter how difficult the problem.

Who's on First?

by Abbott and Costello

ABBOTT: You know, strange as it may seem, they give ballplayers nowadays very peculiar names. Now, on the St. Louis team Who's on first, What's on second, I Don't Know is on third—

COSTELLO: That's what I want to find out. I want you to tell me the names of the fellows on the St. Louis team.

ABBOTT: I'm telling you. Who's on first, What's on second, I Don't Know is on third—

COSTELLO: You know the fellows' names?

ABBOTT: Yes.

COSTELLO: Well, then who's playing first?

ABBOTT: Yes.

COSTELLO: I mean the fellow's name on first base.

ABBOTT: Who.

COSTELLO: The fellow playing first base.

ABBOTT: Who.

COSTELLO: The guy on first base.

ABBOTT: Who is on first.

COSTELLO: Well, what are you asking me for?

ABBOTT: I'm not asking you—I'm telling you. Who is on first.

COSTELLO: I'm asking you—who's on first?

ABBOTT: That's the man's name!

COSTELLO: That's who's name?

ABBOTT: Yes.

COSTELLO: Well, go ahead tell me!

ABBOTT: Who.

COSTELLO: Have you got a first baseman on first?

ABBOTT: Certainly.

COSTELLO: Then who's playing first?

ABBOTT: Absolutely.

COSTELLO: Well, all I'm trying to find out is what's the guy's name on first base.

ABBOTT: Oh, no, no. What is on second base.

COSTELLO: I'm not asking you who's on second.

ABBOTT: Who's on first.

COSTELLO: That's what I'm trying to find out.

ABBOTT: Now, take it easy.

COSTELLO: What's the guy's name on first base?

ABBOTT: What's the guy's name on second base.

COSTELLO: I'm not asking you who's on second.

ABBOTT: Who's on first.

COSTELLO: I don't know.

ABBOTT: He's on third.

COSTELLO: If I mentioned the third baseman's name, who did I say is playing third?

ABBOTT: No, Who's playing first.

COSTELLO: Stay off of first, will you?

ABBOTT: Well, what do you want me to do?

COSTELLO: Now, what's the guy's name on first base?

ABBOTT: What's on second.

COSTELLO: I'm not asking you who's on second.

ABBOTT: Who's on first.

COSTELLO: I don't know.

ABBOTT: He's on third.

COSTELLO: There I go, back to third again.

ABBOTT: Please. Now what is it you want to know?

COSTELLO: What is the fellow's name on third base?

ABBOTT: What is the fellow's name on second base.

COSTELLO: I'm not asking you who's on second.

ABBOTT: Who's on first.

COSTELLO: I don't know. *(Makes noise.)* Do you have an outfield?

ABBOTT: Oh, sure.

COSTELLO: The left fielder's name?

ABBOTT: Why.

COSTELLO: I just thought I'd ask.

ABBOTT: Well, I just thought I'd tell you.

COSTELLO: Then tell me who's playing left field.

ABBOTT: Who's playing first.

COSTELLO: Stay out of the infield. I want to know what's the fellow's name in left field.

ABBOTT: What is on second.

COSTELLO: I'm not asking you who's on second.

ABBOTT: Now take it easy, take it easy.

COSTELLO: And the left fielder's name?

ABBOTT: Why.

COSTELLO: Because.

ABBOTT: Oh, he's centre field.

COSTELLO: Wait a minute. Do you have a pitcher?

ABBOTT: Wouldn't this be a fine team without a pitcher?

COSTELLO: Tell me the pitcher's name.

ABBOTT: Tomorrow.

COSTELLO: You don't want to tell me today?

ABBOTT: I'm telling you, man.

COSTELLO: Then go ahead.

ABBOTT: Tomorrow.

COSTELLO: What time tomorrow are you going to tell me who's pitching?

ABBOTT: Now listen. Who is not pitching. Who is on—

COSTELLO: I'll break your arm if you say who's on first.

ABBOTT: Then why come up here and ask?

COSTELLO: I want to know what's the pitcher's name.

ABBOTT: What's on second.

COSTELLO: You got a catcher?

ABBOTT: Yes.

COSTELLO: The catcher's name?

ABBOTT: Today.

COSTELLO: Today. And Tomorrow's pitching.

ABBOTT: Yes.

COSTELLO: I'm a good catcher too, you know.

ABBOTT: I know that.

COSTELLO: I would like to catch. Tomorrow's pitching and I'm catching.

ABBOTT: Yes.

COSTELLO: Tomorrow throws the ball and the guy up bunts the ball.

ABBOTT: Yes.

COSTELLO: Now when he bunts the ball—me being a good catcher—I want to throw the guy out at first base, so I pick up the ball and throw it to who?

ABBOTT: Now, that's the first thing you've said right.

COSTELLO: I DON'T EVEN KNOW WHAT I'M TALKING ABOUT.

ABBOTT: Well, that's all you have to do.

COSTELLO: Is to throw it to first base.

ABBOTT: Yes.

COSTELLO: Now who's got it?

ABBOTT: Naturally.

COSTELLO: Who has it?

ABBOTT: Naturally.

COSTELLO: OK.

ABBOTT: Now you've got it.

COSTELLO: I pick up the ball and I throw it to Naturally.

ABBOTT: No you don't. You throw the ball to first base.

COSTELLO: Then who gets it?

ABBOTT: Naturally.

COSTELLO: I throw the ball to Naturally.

ABBOTT: You don't. You throw it to Who.

COSTELLO: Naturally.

ABBOTT: Well, naturally. Say it that way.

COSTELLO: I said I'd throw the ball to Naturally.

ABBOTT: You don't. You throw it to Who.

COSTELLO: Naturally.

ABBOTT: Yes.

COSTELLO: So I throw the ball to first base and Naturally gets it.

ABBOTT: No. You throw the ball to first base—

COSTELLO: Then who gets it?

ABBOTT: Naturally.

COSTELLO: That's what I'm saying.

ABBOTT: You're not saying that.

COSTELLO: I throw the ball to first base.

ABBOTT: Then Who gets it.

COSTELLO: He'd better get it.

ABBOTT: That's it. All right now, don't get excited. Take it easy.

COSTELLO: Now I throw the ball to first base, whoever it is grabs the ball, so the guy runs to second.

ABBOTT: Uh-huh.

COSTELLO: Who picks up the ball and throws it to What. What throws it to I Don't Know. I Don't Know throws it back to Tomorrow—a triple play.

ABBOTT: Yeah. It could be.

COSTELLO: Another guy gets up and it's a long fly ball to centre. Why? I don't know. And I don't care.

ABBOTT: What was that?

COSTELLO: I said, I don't-care.

ABBOTT: Oh, that's our shortstop.

COSTELLO: *(Makes noises—steps close to Abbott and they glare at each other.)*

33

Joseph M. Schenck *Presents*

"Buster" Keaton

in

THE GOAT

RELEASED EXCLUSIVELY THROUGH
METRO PICTURES CORPORATION

1

2

3

4

5

6

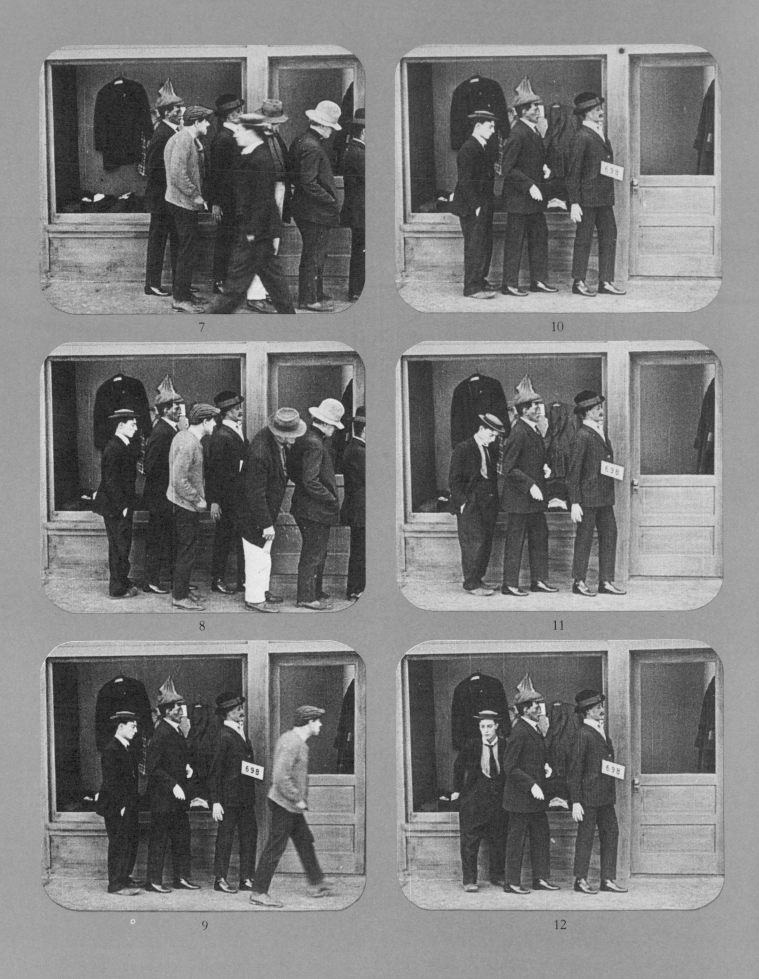

7

8

9

10

11

12

13

14

15

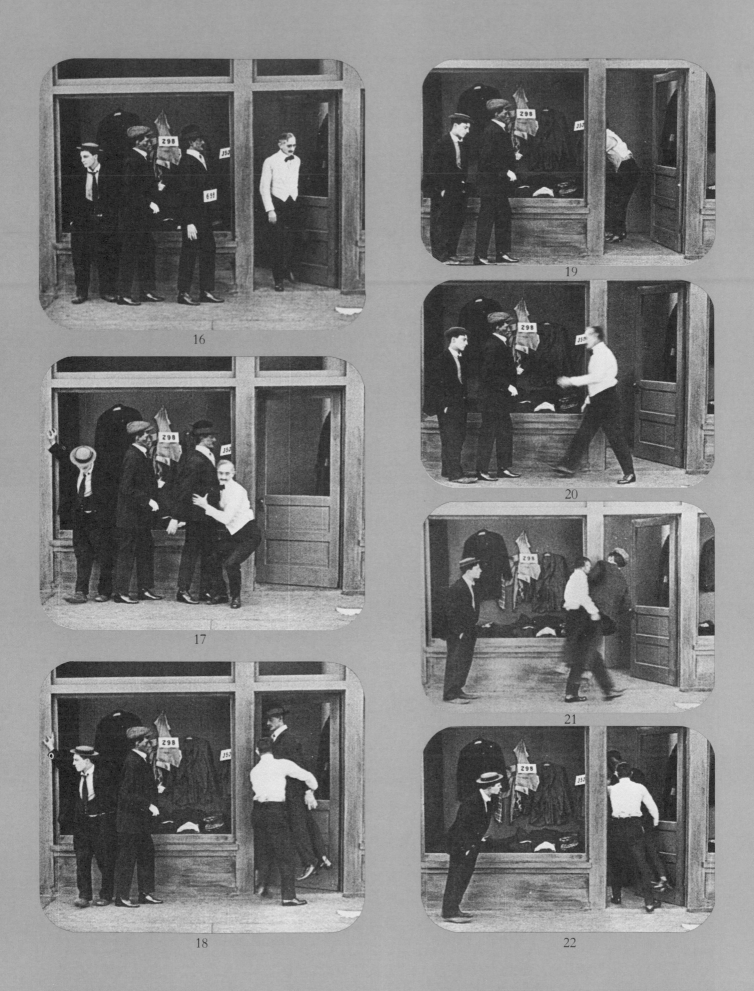

16

17

18

19

20

21

22

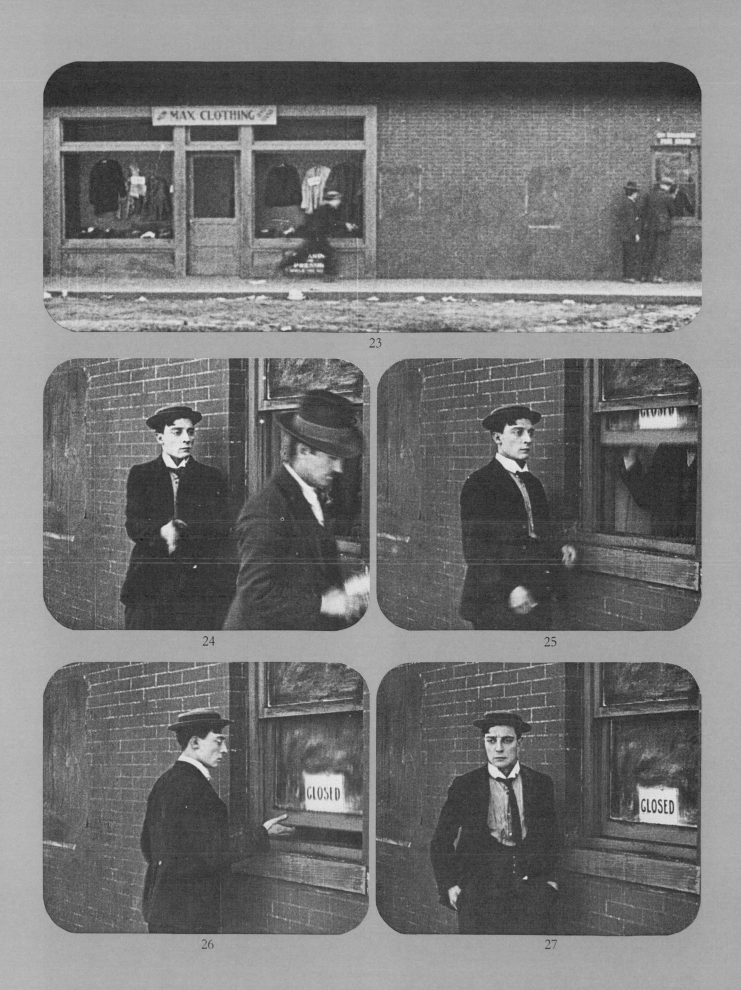

23

24

25

26

27

Clever Fools

by Richard Scrimger

Laughter is like medicine, or sleep. You feel better after it. People who make you laugh are like doctors. Today our doctors of laughter are circus clowns and television comedians. In the Middle Ages the doctors of laughter were called court jesters, or "fools." They wore funny costumes, with bells on their caps and shoes, and parti-colored clothes that didn't match. They carried sticks with balloonlike bladders on the end, to beat people without hurting them. They told jokes and made fun and played tricks . . . and everyone crowded around to watch, and listen, and laugh.

Jesters were not really foolish at all, but very clever. They were "artificial" fools, who lived by their wits. People laughed *with* them, often at someone else.

TRIBOULET

Triboulet, the court jester of Francis I, king of France, loved to mimic a pompous nobleman at the court. The nobleman, who was very tall, would strut up and down, waving his long arms in graceful sweeping motions. And Triboulet, who was very short, would walk behind him, waving his stubby arms jerkily. The nobleman would tap his elegant walking stick on the floor, and Triboulet would lean over to bang his jester's stick, with the flapping balloon on the end. And everyone would roar with laughter.

One day the nobleman turned round and saw the jester. "Why, Triboulet, you rascal!" he cried. "I'll kill you!"

Triboulet ran to the king for protection. "Don't worry," said the king. "If he does kill you, I'll have him executed an hour later."

"An hour *later?*" Triboulet looked up at the king piteously. "Why not an hour *before?*"

MATHURINE

Much of the jesters' work took place at meals. They sang songs and told stories and made jokes while the guests ate their dinner. It must have been hungry work, watching everyone else eat. On her birthday Mathurine, who was jester to the Burgundian court in France, was allowed to eat with the other guests, on one condition: she had to wear a long gaily colored coat. As the meal went on, the guests were surprised to see Mathurine cram as much food into her pockets as she put in her mouth. When she took a whole chicken and hid it under her coat, the duchess of Burgundy had had enough.

"What's this?" she cried. "You're stealing my food!"

"Not at all, Your Grace," replied Mathurine. "You invited me and my coat to dinner. I'm making sure my coat has enough to eat."

Jesters were more than just joke-makers, though. They were people that kings and queens and nobles liked, and paid attention to—and that made them important people. In some courts the "fools" were taken very seriously. In 1502 Alboin, king of Lombardy in Italy, wanted to know which of his nobles he could trust, so he went to his jester for advice.

The jester's name was Bertoldo, and the next day he showed the king a foolproof way of testing the trustworthiness of the nobles at his court.

"Take these, sire," Bertoldo said, pointing to a stack of boxes he had brought with him. "Give one box to each of your nobles, telling them it contains a great secret. They are to return the boxes to you *without* opening them. When the nobles return the boxes,

BERTOLDO

you will know whether they are trustworthy or not."

"How?" asked the king. "What is inside the boxes?"

"Birds," replied the clever Bertoldo.

One of the most famous jesters in history was Nasr ed-Din. He was the fool to Tamburlaine, the emperor who ruled Greece, Turkey, and Afghanistan in the fourteenth century. Whole books have been written about the jokes and funny stories he told—or, occasionally, didn't tell. . . .

"Do you know the story I'm going to tell you now?" he asked the court at supper one day.

"No," they answered.

"Neither do I," he said, and ran out of the dining hall.

The next day he tried again.

"Do you know the story I'm going to tell you now?"

This time the court decided to answer differently.

"Yes," they said.

"Good," said Nasr ed-Din. "Then I don't have to tell it." And he ran away again.

The next day the court was ready for him. "Do you know the story I'm going to tell you now?" he asked.

"Some of us do," they answered, "and some of us don't."

"Well then," said Nasr ed-Din. "Those of you who know the story can tell it to those of you who don't." And he ran off for the third time.

One morning years later Tamburlaine saw his face in a pool of water. It looked so old and ugly that the great emperor burst out crying. For two hours he cried, and all his court cried with him. When at last Tamburlaine stopped crying, his court stopped too—all except Nasr ed-Din. Tamburlaine asked the jester why he was still crying.

"Your Majesty," Nasr ed-Din replied, "you saw your face for a moment, and cried for two hours. But I . . . I have to look at you all day long."

NASR ED-DIN

Now, Tamburlaine might have been upset if one of his nobles had said this to him, but Nasr ed-Din wasn't a noble. He wasn't an important person at all. He was only a court jester—a fool—and so Tamburlaine laughed.

MARCOLF

Court jesters often made fun of kings and queens, pretending that their bell-covered hats were crowns, that their balloon-on-a-stick was really a sceptre, that their "motley" clothes were really royal robes. Usually the kings and queens didn't mind. Maybe they welcomed the chance to laugh at themselves. But sometimes the court jesters went too far; then they might be beaten in earnest, or killed.

One king who didn't like being laughed at was Solomon, who was known for his wisdom. His jester was the famous Marcolf, and there came a day when Marcolf went too far and poked fun at the wise man himself. Solomon banished Marcolf from his sight—but the jester just went to the next room, and hid himself, and continued to shout at the king. So Solomon ordered Marcolf to be hanged. Marcolf begged to be allowed to choose the tree he would be hanged from, and Solomon agreed.

The execution party set out the next day: a hangman with a rope, three guards, and Marcolf. They marched up to the tallest tree on the palace grounds, but Marcolf didn't like it; it was too tall. They suggested another tree, but Marcolf said it wasn't tall enough. The next tree was too thick; the next was the wrong color; the next didn't have enough leaves. And so the hangman, and the three guards, and Marcolf the jester marched through the countryside searching for the right tree, the perfect tree from which to hang Marcolf . . .

None of them were ever seen again, and so a fool came to outwit Solomon, who is called the wisest man who ever lived.

Fools ask questions that wise men cannot answer.
(Italy)

With a foolish head, the legs have no peace.
(Russia)

A fool and his money are soon parted.
(England)

Words of Wisdom

Long whiskers cannot take the place of brains.
(Russia)

Experience is the father of wisdom.
(England)

It is easy to be wise after the event.
(England)

A fool seeks occasions to talk;
A Sage, quietude.
(India)

A hundred wise men think alike,
But never two fools.
(India)

Begging together with a wise man is better than ruling together with a fool.
(India)

The wise man listens to his own mind, the foolish man heeds the mob.
(China)

Take Wing

Fragment of sky
on the snow:
blue jay.

A sudden gust of wind:
dry leaves become

sparrows.

— *by Nancy Prasad*

Watch the Birdie!

by C. K. Dexter Haven

ROSE-BREASTED GROSBEAK

CARDINAL

CANADA WARBLER

One of the nicest things about bird-watching is that you can do it anywhere, anytime—walking to school, looking out the window at your backyard, riding your bike through the park. Everywhere you go, there are birds.

Around your neighborhood you will probably see the same species again and again. In the city, sparrows, pigeons, robins, and starlings are the most common. If you are lucky enough to live in the country, you will be surrounded by a great variety of birds—finches, crows, red-winged blackbirds, thrushes, chickadees, hawks, cowbirds, and many others. But wherever you live, if you keep your eyes and ears open, you can spot new and different types of birds.

You don't need special equipment for bird-watching, but a good pair of binoculars and a field guide will help you get much more out of your hobby.

Look for binoculars marked 7 x 35 or 8 x 40. They are strong enough for you to see birds a good distance away and light enough for you to carry easily. Binoculars are expensive, but you may be able to borrow some or get a second-hand pair at a bargain price.

The following text appears within the field guide image:

COMMON REDPOLL *Carduelis flammea* 5" (13 cm)   M 354
Note the *bright red cap* on the forehead. A little, streaked, gray-brown finch with a *black chin* and dark streaks on the flanks. The male is pink-breasted. In size, shape, and actions, resembles an American Goldfinch or a Pine Siskin.
Similar species: (1) Male House Finch and (2) male Purple Finch are larger, redder, and have red rumps; lack the black chin.
Voice: In flight, a rattling *chet-chet-chet-chet.* Song, a trill, followed by the rattling *chet-chet-chet-chet.*
Range: Circumboreal. Winters irregularly to n. and cen. U.S. East: Map 354. **Habitat:** Birches, tundra scrub. In winter, weeds, brush.
HOARY REDPOLL *Carduelis hornemanni* 5" (13 cm)   M 355
Among Redpolls look for a "frostier" bird with an *unstreaked whitish rump.* In males, rump may be pink-tinged; bill more conical than Common Redpoll's; undertail coverts unstreaked.
Range: Arctic; circumpolar. Winters irregularly to n. U.S. East: Map 355. **Habitat:** Similar to Common Redpoll's.
HOUSE FINCH   M 356
Carpodacus mexicanus 5–5¾" (13–14 cm)
This recent addition to our eastern avifauna is often mistaken for the Purple Finch, with which it may associate at the feeding tray. It is smaller; male brighter red. Note the dark *stripes* on the sides and belly. The striped brown female is distinguished from the female Purple Finch by its smaller bill and bland face pattern (no heavy mustache or dark cheek patch).
Voice: Song, bright, but loose and disjointed; frequently ends in a harsh nasal *wheer* or *che-urr.* Notes, finchlike; some suggest House Sparrow's, but more musical.
Range: W. U.S. to s. Mexico. Introduced in ne. U.S. about 1940; spreading. East: Map 356. **Habitat:** Cities, suburbs, farms.
PURPLE FINCH   M 357
Carpodacus purpureus 5½–6" (14–15 cm)
Like a sparrow dipped in raspberry juice. *Male:* Dull rose-red, brightest on head and rump. *Female and immature:* Heavily striped, brown, sparrowlike. Note the *broad dark jaw stripe,* dark ear patch, broad light stripe behind eye, and largish bill.
Similar species: See House Finch (above).
Voice: Song, a fast lively warble; note, a dull metallic *tick.*
Range: Canada, Pacific states, ne. U.S. Winters to s. U.S. East: Map 357. **Habitat:** Woods, groves; in winter, also suburbs.
PINE GROSBEAK *Pinicola enucleator* 8–10" (20–25 cm) M 358
Near size of Robin; a large tame winter finch with a longish tail. In flight, undulates deeply. *Male, adult:* Dull rose-red, dark wings with 2 white bars. *Male, immature:* Similar to female, but touch of reddish on head and rump. *Female:* Gray, with 2 white wing bars; head and rump tinged dull yellow.
Voice: Call, a whistled *tee-tew-tew,* suggesting that of Greater Yellowlegs, but finchlike; also a musical *chee-vli.*
Range: Boreal forests of N. Hemisphere, wintering irruptively southward. East: Map 358. **Habitat:** Conifer forests; in winter, also mixed woods, fruiting trees.

270   271

Image labels: RED FINCHES etc., orange variant, HOUSE FINCH, COMMON REDPOLL, HOARY REDPOLL, PURPLE FINCH, imm. ♂, PINE GROSBEAK

A field guide is a book written especially for bird-watchers. It has detailed colored pictures of the different species, as well as information about their songs and nests, where they feed, what time of year you can expect to see them, and how they fly. Most field guides are small enough to carry along in your pocket or knapsack.

Once you are familiar with your neighborhood birds, you will want to go on birding expeditions to other locations. Some birds live near marshes, others in the woods, others in fields, still others on lakes or oceans. This is where they find their food and build their nests, and this is where you must go to find them.

The best times to go bird-watching are just after dawn and just before sunset. Birds are most active then. They are busy singing and looking for food.

Imagine that you and a friend are out in the woods. You are scanning the trees carefully. Suddenly you spot a little yellow and black bird.

"Hey! Look over there!" you shout to your friend as you point and run over toward the bird.

Wrong!! By the time your friend looks, the bird is sure to be long gone. And you won't have had a chance to get a good enough look to make a definite identification.

You have just broken the three rules of bird-watching: move slowly, be quiet, look carefully.

Most birds are shy creatures, and any quick movement or noise will frighten them away. When you are looking for birds—listen, don't talk. Move slowly and carefully. Try not to walk on sticks or dry leaves. It is also a good idea not to wear bright-colored clothing, as this makes it easier for the birds to see you.

Now you have learned your lesson. You walk quietly, listening for bird calls. Some birds such as the killdeer and chickadee sing their own name. Many other birds have very distinctive calls that you will soon learn to recognize. The squawk of a blue jay is hard to mistake for the trill of a robin! You stop. A bird is singing. You look around and spot a black and white and red bird sitting on a branch. This time you stand still and slowly raise your binoculars to your eyes. There, now you can see it better. How can you figure out what bird it is?

- Where are the black, white, and red colors? What color is on its wings? On its head? Under its chin?

- How big is it? Is it about the size of a pigeon, or smaller, like a wren?

- What shape is it? Is it fat or slim? Does it have a crest on its head? Does it have a long or short tail?

Oops! The bird flies over to the trunk of a nearby tree. You follow it with your binoculars.

- How did it fly? Did it go straight? Up and down?

- Is it sitting on the trunk with its head up, or is it creeping down the tree headfirst?

- Is it feeding? Some birds feed on the trunks of trees; others feed on the ground; others pick seeds from branches; others drink out of flowers.

You can see how carefully you must observe in order to identify your bird. If all this seems like a lot to think about, don't worry. You will soon find your eyes getting sharper. And the more birds you learn to recognize, the easier it is to spot and identify new species.

You don't have to go out in the woods to watch birds. If you have a yard, there are many ways of attracting feathered visitors.

In the spring, you can buy or build birdhouses for them to make their nests in. Birds also enjoy water for drinking and baths, so you may want to put out a birdbath for them. Remember to change the water every few days and keep it clean.

In the winter, when food is hard to find, birds will flock to your yard if you put food out on the ground or in a feeder. Birds like suet, cracked nuts, corn, sunflower seeds, peanut butter, and seeds in their menu. Remem-

ber, though: once you start putting out food for birds, you should keep it up all winter. Your feathered friends will come to depend on you for their daily food.

When birds get used to coming to your yard, you may even get some of the less timid ones to eat right out of your hand. Put some sunflower seeds in your hand, hold it away from your body, and stand very still near your birdfeeder. In a few minutes a friendly chickadee might land on your hand and pick out a seed to eat. Having a bird so close and feeling its little claws hanging onto your finger is a real thrill!

Kay McKeever
and the
Owls

It is almost dusk, and as I turn away from the window beside my desk, the last light of day reflects an orange glow from the eyes of a big owl sitting behind my chair. I lean back for a moment and blow softly into her neck feathers. She grunts contentedly and closes her eyes, as if to savor the moment. When I stop, the owl opens her eyes to see why. Then she nibbles gently at my hair and around my ears. This is Granny, a Spectacled Owl. Not knowing that she and I are different kinds of creatures, Granny thinks I am her mate.

Although Granny is very special to me and my husband, Larry, she is only one of over a hundred owls of all sizes and types that share our lives. We operate a place called The Owl Rehabilitation Research Foundation in the Jordan Valley of Southern Ontario. Our windows overlook a wide river estuary bordered by cat-tail marshes and filled with water lilies. Our house is on a high bank covered with tall oak and hickory, ash and white pine. I lived in this valley years and years ago, when I was a little girl, and now I am happy to be back home again.

When we decided to move back to this valley, it wasn't just to sit and admire the scenery. Larry and I came back to work. Over the years we realized that something very worrisome was happening to wildlife, especially to the animals who control the numbers of other creatures below them in the food chain by preying upon them. These predators were rapidly disappearing.

The cause of the problem was people. People were cutting down the forests and ploughing the prairies and draining the swamps. The land was being bulldozed and covered with big shopping malls, houses, and factories. Millions of animals were being killed every year along our highways by high-speed trucks and cars. These fast-moving killers are especially dangerous for night creatures such as foxes, raccoons, and owls. Blinded by headlights, they don't see the big machines behind the terrible glare. As if all this wasn't bad enough, some irresponsible people were shooting, trapping, and poisoning the predators as well.

Upset by the slaughter, Larry and I decided to try to help at least one kind of predator survive in a world of people. We decided on owls—or, to be more accurate, one small owl helped us decide on helping owls.

The owl responsible was a nestling Screech Owl that had been stolen from its parents and then turned over to our local Humane Society. There was nothing they could do to help it, so we persuaded them to let us try. We borrowed library books about raising wildlife but there wasn't much about owls. The books said that insects, worms, and mice were good for Screech Owls. We scurried around trying to catch some mice and moths, without much success. The worms were easier—we had big dew-worms in our cherry orchard. But to our horror, the little owl sickened and died in just ten days.

When I gave the Screech Owl's little body to an ornithologist and asked what had happened, he told me that our big dew-worms were contaminated by the pesticides farmers spray on their fruit trees. I was broken-hearted to think I had accidentally killed our tiny owl with poisoned food.

This sad experience prompted Larry and me to begin to plan how we could use the rest of our lives to help wild owls. Gradually, as word of our interest in injured owls spread, the frightened victims of our urban world began to turn up at our door in odd-shaped boxes and baskets and even feed sacks. And, almost as frightened as our patients, we entered the world of veterinarians and their operating rooms and their instructions for home care and medication. We began to learn what rehabilitation was all about; saving some, losing some, seeing the quiet suffering, and always being touched by the beauty and dignity of these wild creatures.

That was more than fifteen years ago, and we are still "up to our eyes" in owls. Over a hundred new arrivals come to us every year from all parts of Canada and the United States. They arrive by car and air express, and almost half of them will be rehabilitated. When they leave us, these owls have a good chance of surviving again in the wild. We always try to release them near their original homes, even if that means the other side of the continent.

Other owls never leave us. Although we can help them back to good health, they never regain full use of a damaged wing or eye. Some of these injured owls are the most important owls we have. They "mother" orphaned juveniles so that the young owls grow up normally and can be released back into the wild again. These injured "substitute parents" are the owls you'll read about in this book, *Granny's Gang.* Like Granny, many of them live with us and think they're part of the family.

Raising and rehabilitating hundreds of owls hasn't been easy. We have had to build more than fifty outdoor compounds, great big flight cages much larger than rooms in human houses. They contain pools and trees, stumps, special perches, and nest boxes or

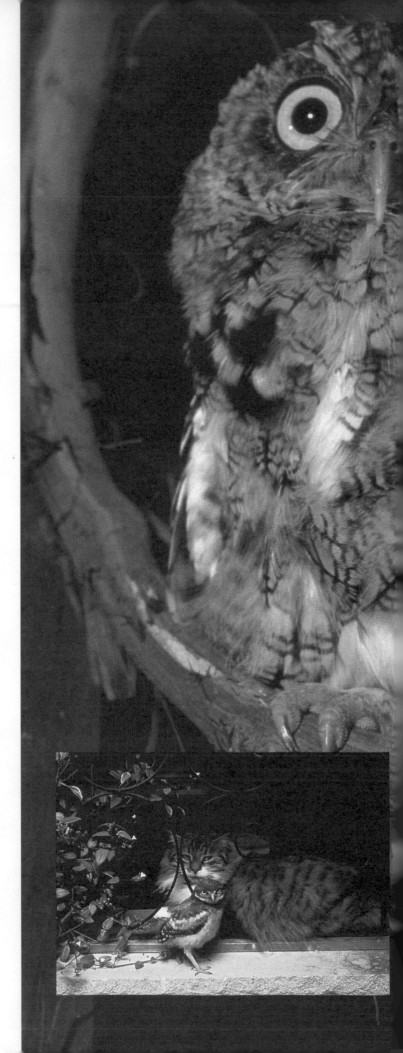

platforms. There are only two or three owls in each compound, and we make sure they have lots of places to hide—from us and from each other, if they want to. Most of all, we have to give them the best food for owls, and that means *mice!* I never dreamed we'd need so many mice! When there are 125 owls staying here, we need about 250 mice every day! Because we could never catch that many ourselves, we drive hundreds of kilometres every week to pick them up from breeding laboratories. In case of emergencies, we keep a small colony of breeding mice ourselves. That way we always have a fresh mouse for a newly arrived baby owl or owl that's badly injured.

Finally, we have to raise a lot of money every year to buy the mice and build the cages, to pay for surgery, medications, air express from distant places, and long distance telephone calls. Raising that much money, chauffeuring owls around, and picking up mice takes most of Larry's time, although he tries to do a lot of other things too. Most of my time is spent cleaning. I clean the owl cages and the mouse basins and the house. And in the evening, if my cleaning is done and the owls are tended to, I work at my desk, keeping notes on all the owls' activities for that day.

So here I am, this lovely spring evening, with Granny watching over my shoulder as I write. I hope you will enjoy reading about the owls that have enriched our lives as much as we have enjoyed living with them. And while you are laughing at their antics, maybe even shedding a tear, I hope you will come to think of them as unique and beautiful creatures. Then, perhaps you could help other people to see them this way too.

The Captive

by *Tot Jones*

Saturday

Dear Hank:

You won't believe what's happening in the woods! This morning some noise outside woke me. I went out on the deck, and there were about five blue jays swooping at something and screaming their heads off. They flew away after a while, and I could see what was bothering them. There was an enormous hawk sitting up there on a limb. He would spread his wings, start to fly off, and then settle back on the limb. He kept doing that, and the blue jays came back and screamed at him some more—you should have seen it!

You remember that our new house is built on stilts and hangs over a wooded ravine. Well, this hawk was on a limb only about six metres above the bedroom deck, so I could really get a good look at him. I ran and told Mom and Dad what was going on, and Mom found the bird book, and we went out again. We looked at all the different hawks in the book and decided it was a red-tailed hawk. Some of them are sixty-five centimetres long and have a wingspread of more than a metre. That bird looked like an airplane ready to take off when he spread his wings!

We couldn't figure out why the hawk didn't fly away instead of letting those dumb blue jays pick on him. Hawks fly through our woods lots of times and maybe stop and rest on a limb, but they hardly ever stay very long.

Just before lunch Dad got out his field glasses and let me look first. You won't believe what I saw!

The hawk has leather straps on his legs, and one loop is hung up on a tree snag. *That hawk is trapped up there!*

I'll keep you posted. Write!

Your pal,

David

Sunday

Dear Hank:

I wanted to get your letter in the mail yesterday, so I am writing again today to let you know what's happening with our hawk. Mom worried about him starving to death up there, so we checked the bird book to see what red-tailed hawks usually eat. Among other things, they like fowl. Mom had a chicken in the fridge, and she said the bird could have the neck and gizzard and all those weird things. It took a while to figure out how we could get the food up to him.

Dad figured that the hawk was a trained bird, so we checked the encyclopedia (wow, had to look that one up) to see what we could find under falconry. That's the art of training hawks to hunt, in case you didn't know. Well, after reading about lures, I got the idea of tying the chicken neck to a rope and trying to sling it over the limb the bird is sitting on. At least he could get some bites out of it.

Well, you remember what a great shot I am—my first shot missed by quite a bit, but the next one wasn't too bad. The rope went over the limb just past the hawk, and I pulled it slowly so it would slide up beside him. Well, at first the poor bird kept hopping on his free leg and making funny noises, but he finally settled down and looked at the neck. Then he started tearing pieces out of it. We all yelled and clapped, which scared him even more, but at least he had some food for the night.

This morning he was still there, and we knew we had to find his owner, or falconer, as the encyclopedia says. Since it was Sunday, the state wildlife office was closed, but Dad had a thought—why not call the zoo? So he did, and they gave him the number of a man who had a list of all the falconers in the whole state. Dad called him for hours, and finally, late in the afternoon, he answered his phone and he actually knew whose hawk it was. I guess when a trained bird gets loose, all the falconers in the area hear about it. Anyway, he said the hawk was a female named Fay. He asked for our address and phone number and said he would try to reach her owner right away.

Later I tied the chicken gizzard to the rope and, after a few tries, managed to sling it up to Fay. It didn't take her more than a minute to devour it.

It's getting dark, and we still haven't heard anything from Fay's owner. Guess she'll have to spend another night up there. At least the blue jays have stopped bugging her.

I'll keep you posted,

David

Monday (Thank goodness for vacations.)

Dear Hank:

This was probably the most exciting day of my life! The bird's owner called early this morning. He'd spent all day Sunday searching for Fay, and that's why nobody could get him on the phone. Anyway, he said he was on his way over, so I figured there was no need to scare the bird with any more rope slinging.

Frank, Fay's owner, was here before we finished breakfast. What a neat guy! He told us a little about Fay. I guess it's not as common to train a red-tailed hawk as a falcon, but Frank says she's a winner.

Frank kept talking to Fay, and she hopped around a little and looked excited. He had some equipment with him—a big leather glove to carry her on, a little hood she wears, a whistle, and a leash. He said he really needed to be two people, one to get up there and free her, and one to be on the deck to whistle her down.

I asked if he thought she would attack me if I climbed the tree and unhooked her. He described what a hawk's talons could do to a hand—and I wasn't so brave any more. Then I asked him what would happen if I got on a limb above her and unhooked her with something from there. Then she couldn't touch me.

He thought it might work and asked Dad how he felt about it. Dad wasn't all that thrilled, and I thought Mom was going to have a fit. They finally said OK, but to be careful.

Well, good old Dad, the inventor, decided he could strap some kind of hook onto his ball retriever, that thing he uses to get golf balls out of the lake. It looks real short but slides out to about two metres when it's extended. We figured I could stick it through my belt while I was climbing, so I could have my hands free.

It was a piece of cake climbing up there (I'd done it before), but the closer I came, the more nervous Fay got. She watched me like a hawk! (Get it?) Frank was talking to her all the time, which helped. Finally I got to the limb above her, and the ball retriever reached her branch easily. I could see where her leg strap was caught, and I only needed to get my hook through it and pull it toward me to release her.

Frank had told me to let him know the second I got the hook through her strap, so I slipped it through, called to Frank, and pulled, all at the same time. He blew his whistle, Fay took off, flew in two circles, and swooped down straight at Frank's glove. He had something on his glove for her to eat, and she pulled on it like someone starving. When she was finished, he slipped the hood over her head, and it was all over.

The ball retriever is at the bottom of the ravine. I dropped it when Fay took off, and I almost fell out of the tree myself, trying to get down there fast so I could get a close look at Fay. She is really a beautiful bird and holds her head up like a queen. She is three years old, sort of reddish brown, and *huge!*

Frank really thanked us and invited us to come out and watch Fay train anytime. I can't wait.

Well, you finally wrote a letter—glad you guys creamed the Patriots. The old soccer team must be surviving without me after all.

Can't wait until your next visit. Maybe we can go out and watch Fay train. Tell the gang hello.

Your friend,

David

As Dead As a Dodo

by Shawn Rice

THE DODO

Raphus Cucullatus

THE PASSENGER PIGEON

Ectopistes Migratorius

Nanabozho and the Wild Geese

by Dorothy M. Reid

Nanabozho lived with his grandmother in a small *wigwam* in the forest. He could swim better and run faster than any of the other boys, and he excelled them too in pranks. He loved to swim underwater and jerk the fishermen's lines; he delighted in springing the women's rabbit snares.

One day, as he was wandering through the woods looking for mischief, he came to the shore of a small lake. He saw some bright red berries in the lake and tried to pick them, but all he got was a handful of chilling water that slipped through his fingers.

"I *will* have some," he shouted impatiently and jumped into the lake. He splashed about but could find no berries. Then he glanced upward and caught sight of the fruit hanging from a bush on shore. It was their reflection he had seen. Feeling very foolish, he stamped out of the water.

While he was munching the berries he heard a great tumult of wings over his head. He looked up and saw a flock of geese. They were weary after their journey from the North where they had spent the summer, and were wheeling overhead preparing to land on the lake. Nanabozho hurried in the direction of their flight and saw the birds come to rest on the water with a great flurry and folding of wings. Now he would have a great feast. But first he had to contrive a scheme to capture as many as possible, for if he dashed in among them he would catch only one or two. Going quickly but quietly back into the woods, he peeled off strips of cedar bark and made a long rope which he coiled in his hand. Then he slipped cautiously into the water, being careful not to disturb the weary birds. He swam under them and tied their legs together with his cedar rope. At the same time he tied each goose to the next one so that he could pull them all up on shore together.

At first all went well, for Nanabozho was so cunning and swift that the geese did not notice him or know what was happening. But his greed betrayed him. Instead of being content with a few geese, he went on to tie up the whole flock, and just as he was finishing, he had to come up for air. He made such a loud whoosh when he inhaled that the geese took fright. The first goose to fly up was in the middle of the rope and all the others followed. As they rose from the lake they formed a V because they were tied together, and Nanabozho dangled at one end. He shouted to the birds to stop, but the geese only beat the air more desperately with their strong gray wings. Already he was far above the treetops, which looked very sharp and unyielding. Just then the birds flew over

a stretch of soft swampy ground. Nanabozho let go of the rope with a shout and landed in a bed of oozing mud.

As for the geese, they continued on their way, still flying in a V because of the rope that joined them together. Wild geese have been flying that way ever since, as you can see if you look up into the autumn sky when they go calling past. Some think there is a note of sadness in their cry, but others believe it is derisive, that they are mocking Nanabozho for failing in his trick.

It was not long before Nanabozho forgot the foolish side of his adventure. All he remembered was that he had flown through the air. He composed a song to celebrate his feat, a song he never tired of singing:

Flocks of wild geese up in the sky,
Nanabozho flew as far and as high.

The people listened respectfully to Nanabozho's song, but whenever he was out of hearing they sang a different one:

High in the autumn sky
Wild geese are calling.
Down from the autumn sky
Nana is falling.

From Sandia Mountain to Sky Pueblo

by Byrd Baylor

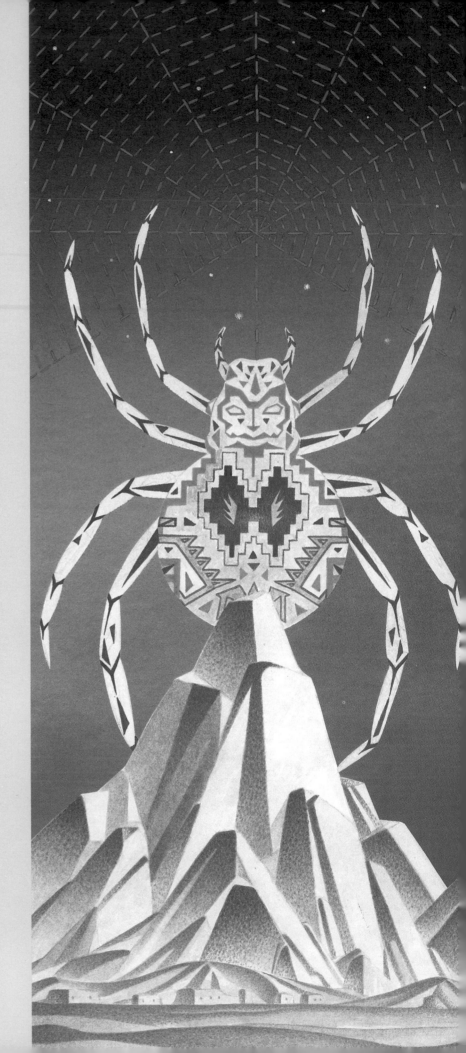

Up on Sandia Mountain
Spider Woman has her home.

Once long ago a man
from Sandia Pueblo
climbed up there to ask
for Spider Woman's help.

He said his wife
had been stolen away
and taken to a pueblo in the sky
where he could never go.

Spider Woman spun a web
that reached from the mountain
straight up through the stars
to Sky Pueblo.
Hidden by darkness,
they travelled along
that gleaming spiderweb bridge.

The man found his wife
and they hurried back over the web
to the mountain
and down to their home
in the valley.

When Spider Woman pulled her web
out of the sky
there was no way for anyone up there
to guess how they had come . . . or gone.

Wardrobes, Trapdoors, Cats' Eyes, and Caves

The wind blew hard
It blew me away
It blew me back to yesterday
It blew tomorrow to today
It blew me to this day behind
It blew me to another time.

Now I'm stuck in yesterday
And there I guess I'll have to stay
Until it blows me back away
Until it blows me to today.

from "Today and Yesterday"
— by Robert Heidbreder

FANTASY WORLDS

FIVE CHILDREN
AND IT

gician's
hew

LEWIS

The
BORROWERS
MARY NORTON
ILLUSTRATED BY BETH AND JOE KRUSH

THE
ENORMOUS
EGG
Oliver Butterworth
Illustrated by Louis Darling

Sylvester
and the
Magic Pebble

MACAROON
JULIA CUNNINGHAM

CLIVE KING
Stig of the Dump
Illustrated by Edward Ardizzone

A DELL YEARLING BOOK
The story of an unusual friendship
Felice Holman
The
Cricket
Winter
Illustrated by Ralph Pinto

Half
Magic
Edgar Eager
Edward
Eager

THE
SECRET GARDEN

Margaret Laurence
The Olden Days Coat
Illustrated by Muriel Wood

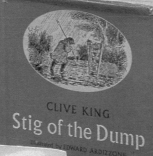

Stuck fast
in Yesterday

RIKAS-KASHA

Chitty Chitty Bang Bang

by Ian Fleming

Commander Pott's twelve-cylinder, eight-litre, supercharged Paragon Panther automobile named herself. The first time she started she sneezed twice, CHITTY-CHITTY and then came two explosions, BANG-BANG. The Pott family soon found out that their car could do something much more marvellous than give two sneezes and two explosions to get started.

The next day was a Saturday and the month was August and the sun positively streamed down. It was a roaster of a day, and at breakfast Commander Pott made an announcement. "Today," he said, "is going to be a roaster, a scorcher. There's only one thing to do, and that's for us to take a delicious picnic and climb into CHITTY-CHITTY-BANG-BANG and dash off down the Dover road to the sea."

Of course everyone was delighted with the idea and while Commander Pott and Jeremy and Jemima went to get CHITTY-CHITTY-BANG-BANG ready, fill her up with petrol, check the water in the radiator, verify the oil in the sump, test the tyre pressures, clean yesterday's squashed flies off the wind-screen, dust down the body and polish up the chromium until it shone like silver, Mimsie filled a hamper with hard-boiled eggs, cold sausages, bread-and-butter sandwiches, jam puffs (with, of course, like all good jam puffs, more jam than puff) and bottles and bottles of the best fizzy lemonade and orange squash.

Then they all piled into the car, with the hood down of course, and, with CHITTY-CHITTY-BANG-BANG's usual two sneezes and two small explosions, they were off up the lane to the motorway that led towards

Dover and to the sea some thirty kilometres away.

But, but, but! And once again but!!

Twenty-two thousand, six hundred and fifty-four other motor cars full of families (that was the number announced by the Automobile Association the next day) had also decided to drive down the Dover road

from Chitty Chitty Bang Bang: The Magical Car

to the sea on that beautiful Saturday morning, and there was an endless stream of cars going the same way as the Pott family in CHITTY-CHITTY-BANG-BANG.

Well, Commander Pott drove as cleverly as he could, overtaking when it was safe, weaving like a snake in and out of the traffic, and taking shortcuts and sideroads to dodge really bad queues of cars, but they made terribly slow progress, in spite of much polite mooing of the boa-constrictor horn and, I'm sorry to say, an occasional furious "GA—GOOOO—GA" on the klaxon when some booby in a black-beetle insisted on hogging it down the middle of the road and not leaving room for CHITTY-CHITTY-BANG-BANG to get by. As for doing a hundred kilometres an hour, there just wasn't any question of it, and they crawled along at a miserable thirty. All of them, Commander Pott, Mimsie, Jeremy, and Jemima, were getting more and more hot

and impatient, and even CHITTY-CHITTY-BANG-BANG began steaming angrily out of the top of her radiator, on which (I'd forgotten to tell you this) there was a silver mascot of a small aeroplane whose propeller went round and round in the wind, faster or slower according to their speed.

And, although they couldn't see them, CHITTY-CHITTY-BANG-BANG's big headlamp eyes, that had been so gleaming with happiness and enthusiasm ever since the day before, began to get angrier and angrier and more and more impatient, so that the people who had gazed in admiration at her through the back windows of their cars became more and more nervous of this gleaming green monster behind them, beginning to look as if she wanted to eat up, with the silver jaws of her radiator, all the line upon line of black-beetle cars that were getting in her way and keeping her family from their picnic by the sea.

But all the same, they were making steady though very slow progress until, outside Canterbury, they came upon a solid jam of cars that must have reached for at least a kilometre. And there they were—stuck at the back of the queue; it really looked as if they couldn't possibly get down to the sands and the sea in time for their picnic, let alone have a wonderful bathe before it.

Suddenly Commander Pott happened to glance at the dashboard, over on the left, opposite Mimsie, and he said excitedly, "I say, all of you, look at that!"

And Mimsie looked and Jeremy and Jemima peered over the back of the seat, and amongst all the knobs and instruments a light on top of a small knob was flashing pale pink! And it was showing a word, and the word said "PULL"!

"Good heavens!" said Commander Pott. "I wondered what that knob was for, but it's one of the ones I haven't had time to tinker with. What can it be for?"

"Look!" cried Mimsie. "The light's turning red!"

And sure enough it was, and now another word was showing! And do you know what the other word said? It said "IDIOT"! So now the angry red knob read "PULL IDIOT"! And Commander Pott laughed out loud and said, "Well I never! That's pretty good cheek! Here's CHITTY-CHITTY-BANG-BANG taking control and calling me an idiot into the bargain! Oh, well! Here goes!" And he reached over and pulled down the little silver lever.

The children, in fact the whole family, sat on the tips of their behinds, if you see what I mean, and waited excitedly to see what would happen.

And a kind of soft humming noise began. It seemed to come from all over the car—from the front axle and from the back axle and from underneath the bonnet. And then the most extraordinary transmogrifications (which is just a long word for "changes") began to occur. The big front mudguards swivelled outwards so that they stuck out like wings, sharply swept back, and the smaller back mudguards did the same (it was lucky the road was wide and there was single-lane traffic, or a neighboring car or a telegraph-pole might have been sliced in half by the sharp green wings!) The wings locked into position with a click and at the same time, though the family couldn't see it from behind, the big radiator grill slid open like a sliding door, and the big propeller of the fan belt, together with the flywheel underneath that runs the petrol pump and the electric generator, slowly slid forward until they were sticking right out in front of the bonnet of the car.

And then, on the dashboard, beside another little lever a *green* light started to blink and this light said "PULL DOWN," and Commander Pott, rather nervously but this time obediently, reached over and gingerly pulled the lever very, very slowly down.

And then, in heaven's name, what do you think happened?

Yes, you're right, absolutely right. The wings slowly tilted, and as Commander Pott, at last realizing what CHITTY-CHITTY-BANG-BANG was up to, pressed down the accelerator pedal, the big green car, which was now what I might call an aerocar, tilted up her shining green and silver nose and took off! Yes! She took off like an aeroplane and soared up over the car in front, just missing her roof, and roared away over the long line of stationary cars in the queue, while all the

people stared out of their car windows in absolute astonishment and Commander Pott called out, "Hang on, everyone. For heaven's sake, hang on!" Mimsie and Jeremy and Jemima clutched the arm-rests beside them and just sat, stiff with excitement and with their eyes and their mouths wide open, thinking, Heavens above! What is going to happen next?

Well, what happened next was that there came a shrill whine of machinery and a thump, thump, thump, thump from under the car, and automatically the four wheels retracted up into the body-work, so as to be out of the way and let the aerocar go faster without the wind resistance of the wheels to slow her down.

Commander Pott sat gripping the wheel and chuckling with excitement and delight. "I told you so!'" he shouted against the roar of the wind. "She's got ideas of her own. She's a magical car. Don't worry! She'll look after us!"

He carefully turned the wheel to see what would happen. And sure enough, the bonnet of the car followed what he did, and after curving about a bit to get the feel of the steering, Commander Pott made straight for the tall tower of Canterbury Cathedral in the distance, soaring over the long line of cars in which the poor people were roasting in the sunshine and sniffing up the disgusting petrol fumes of the cars in front.

Gradually, as they got confidence, Mimsie and Jeremy and Jemima sat back more comfortably in their seats, and Jemima's golden hair streamed out in the wind like a golden flag behind the car and Jeremy's black mop blew about like a golliwog in a hurricane.

Over the solid line of cars they flew—altitude one hundred and fifty metres, air speed one hundred and sixty kilometres

per hour, engine temperature fifty degrees, outside temperature twenty-one degrees, revolutions of propeller three thousand per minute, visibility eight kilometres—over the river that runs through Canterbury down to the coast, over the houses and over the fields where the cows and the horses and the sheep stampeded about at the roaring noise of this big green dragon they had never seen before, and the shadow of CHITTY-CHITTY-BANG-BANG chased after them over the ground.

Over Canterbury, Commander Pott insisted on circling the tall tower of the cathedral, so that the jackdaws and pigeons flew out of their nooks and crannies, squawking and cooing with fright and excitement, and then they headed on over the trees and woods, taking a shortcut away from the crowded Dover road, towards the distant majesty of Dover Castle, with its Union Jack flying from the topmost tower.

And of course, at that speed, in minutes they were over the castle, and again Commander Pott insisted on circling round so that the family (and CHITTY-CHITTY-BANG-BANG for the matter of that) could have a good look, and all the soldiers drilling on the square inside the castle walls looked up, much to the rage of their sergeant-major, and the sentries too, and between you and me, I think CHITTY-CHITTY-BANG-BANG was lucky to get away without being shot at by the soldiers, because after all she had no proper aircraft markings, only her GEN II registration plates, and for all the soldiers knew she might have been some new kind of foreign aeroplane come to attack the castle, or even a flying bomb, which was really quite what she looked like.

But all went well, and they flew on up the coast, looking for a place to land to have their picnic beside the sparkling blue sea. But everywhere—St Margaret's Bay, Walmer, Deal, Sandwich, Ramsgate—all the beaches were crowded with families who had had the same idea as the Pott family, and CHITTY-CHITTY-BANG-BANG's passengers became more and more gloomy as they saw the beautiful sands with their bathers and paddlers and shrimpers, and the rock-pools that were certainly crawling with exciting crabs and eels and valuable shells, all crowded with rival holidaymakers. And they all longed for a bathe and to unpack the bulging picnic basket full of Mimsie's delicious goodies.

Then a curious thing happened. The steering wheel twisted, actually twisted in Commander Pott's hands, as if CHITTY-CHITTY-BANG-BANG realized their disappointment and was taking control herself, and do you know what? CHITTY-CHITTY-BANG-BANG turned away from the coast and soared away over the English Channel *straight out to sea*.

The Walrus and the Carpenter

by Lewis Carroll

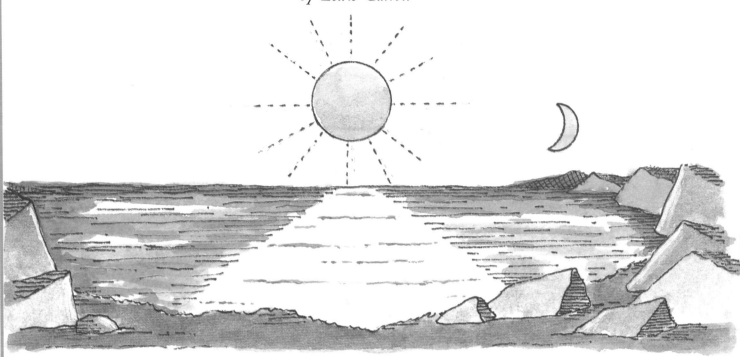

The sun was shining on the sea,
    Shining with all his might:
He did his very best to make
    The billows smooth and bright—
And this was odd, because it was
    The middle of the night.

The moon was shining sulkily,
    Because she thought the sun
Had got no business to be there
    After the day was done—
"It's very rude of him," she said,
    "To come and spoil the fun!"

The sea was wet as wet could be,
    The sands were dry as dry.
You could not see a cloud, because
    No cloud was in the sky:
No birds were flying overhead—
    There were no birds to fly.

The Walrus and the Carpenter
    Were walking close at hand;
They wept like anything to see
    Such quantities of sand:
"If this were only cleared away,"
    They said, "it *would* be grand!"

"If seven maids with seven mops
    Swept it for half a year,
Do you suppose," the Walrus said,
    "That they could get it clear?"
"I doubt it," said the Carpenter,
    And shed a bitter tear.

"O Oysters, come and walk with us!"
    The Walrus did beseech.
"A pleasant walk, a pleasant talk,
    Along the briny beach:
We cannot do with more than four,
    To give a hand to each."

from Through the Looking-Glass

The eldest Oyster looked at him.
    But never a word he said:
The eldest Oyster winked his eye,
    And shook his heavy head—
Meaning to say he did not choose
    To leave the oyster-bed.

But four young oysters hurried up,
    All eager for the treat:
Their coats were brushed, their faces washed,
    Their shoes were clean and neat—
And this was odd, because, you know,
    They hadn't any feet.

Four other Oysters followed them,
    And yet another four;
And thick and fast they came at last,
    And more, and more, and more—
All hopping through the frothy waves,
    And scrambling to the shore.

The Walrus and the Carpenter
    Walked on a mile or so,
And then they rested on a rock
    Conveniently low:
And all the little Oysters stood
    And waited in a row.

"The time has come," the Walrus said,
    "To talk of many things:
Of shoes—and ships—and sealing-wax—
    Of cabbages—and kings—
And why the sea is boiling hot—
    And whether pigs have wings."

"But wait a bit," the Oysters cried,
    "Before we have our chat;
For some of us are out of breath,
    And all of us are fat!"
"No hurry!" said the Carpenter.
    They thanked him much for that.

"A loaf of bread," the Walrus said,
  "Is what we chiefly need:
Pepper and vinegar besides
  Are very good indeed—
Now if you're ready, Oysters dear,
  We can begin to feed."

"But not on us!" the Oysters cried,
  Turning a little blue,
"After such kindness, that would be
  A dismal thing to do!"
"The night is fine," the Walrus said.
  "Do you admire the view?

"It was so kind of you to come!
  And you are very nice!"
The Carpenter said nothing but
  "Cut us another slice:
I wish you were not quite so deaf—
  I've had to ask you twice!"

"It seems a shame," the Walrus said,
  "To play them such a trick,
After we've brought them out so far,
  And made them trot so quick!"
The Carpenter said nothing but
  "The butter's spread too thick!"

"I weep for you," the Walrus said,
  "I deeply sympathize."
With sobs and tears he sorted out
  Those of the largest size,
Holding his pocket-handkerchief
  Before his streaming eyes.

"O Oysters," said the Carpenter.
  "You've had a pleasant run!
Shall we be trotting home again?"
  But answer came there none—
And this was scarcely odd, because
  They'd eaten every one.

In a Hole in the Ground

from The Hobbit
by J.R.R. Tolkien

In a hole in the ground there lived a hobbit. Not a nasty, dirty, wet hole, filled with the ends of worms and an oozy smell, nor yet a dry, bare, sandy hole with nothing in it to sit down on or to eat: it was a hobbit-hole, and that means comfort.

It had a perfectly round door like a porthole, painted green, with a shiny yellow brass knob in the exact middle. The door opened on to a tube-shaped hall like a tunnel: a very comfortable tunnel without smoke, with panelled walls, and floors tiled and carpeted, provided with polished chairs, and lots and lots of pegs for hats and coats—the hobbit was fond of visitors. The tunnel wound on and on, going fairly but not quite straight into the side of the hill—The Hill, as all the people for many miles round called it—and many little round doors opened out of it, first on one side and then on another. No going upstairs for the hobbit: bedrooms, bathrooms, cellars, pantries (lots of these), wardrobes (he had whole rooms devoted to clothes), kitchens, dining rooms, all were on the same floor, and indeed on the same passage. The best rooms were all on the left-hand side (going in), for these were the only ones to have windows, deep-set round windows looking over his garden, and meadows beyond, sloping down to the river.

This hobbit was a very well-to-do hobbit, and his name was Baggins. The Bagginses had lived in the neighborhood of The Hill for time out of mind, and people considered them very respectable, not only because most of them were rich, but also because they never had any adventures or did anything unexpected: you could tell what a Baggins would say on any question without the bother of asking him.

The mother of our particular hobbit—what is a hobbit? I suppose hobbits need some description nowadays, since they have become rare and shy of the Big People, as they call us. They are (or were) small people, smaller than dwarfs (and they have no beards) but very much larger than lilliputians. There is little or no magic about them, except the ordinary everyday sort which helps them to disappear quietly and quickly when large stupid folk like you and me come blundering along, making a noise like elephants which they can hear a mile off. They are inclined to be fat in the stomach; they dress in bright colors (chiefly green and yellow); wear no shoes, because their feet grow natural leathery soles and thick warm brown hair like the stuff on their heads (which is curly); have long clever brown fingers, good-natured faces, and laugh deep fruity laughs (especially after dinner, which they have twice a day when they can get it).

The Visitors

by Lloyd Alexander

Gareth was a black cat with orange eyes. Sometimes, when he hunched his shoulders and put down his ears, he looked like an owl. When he stretched, he looked like a trickle of oil or a pair of black silk pyjamas. When he sat on a window ledge, his eyes half-shut and his tail curled around him, he looked like a secret.

He belonged to a boy named Jason, who loved him and believed Gareth could do anything in the world. As things turned out, Jason was right—not entirely, but almost.

It happened this way.

In the middle of a sunny afternoon, Jason sat in his room on the end of his bed, with his chin in his hands, and wished the past five minutes had never happened.

Downstairs, in that space of time, he had accomplished the following:

1/ Spilled paint on the dining-room table.
2/ Dropped his model airplane and stepped on it.
3/ Coated the inside of one pocket of his jacket with glue, when the tube he had been saving for emergencies had come uncapped.
4/ Torn his shirt.
5/ Punched his younger brother in the ribs for laughing at him.
6/ Talked back to his mother, who had not agreed his brother needed punching.
7/ Begun to cry, a thing Jason despised because he considered himself too old for it.

There had been other details he preferred to forget. In any case, he had been told to go to his room, which he did, feeling put down and miserably sorry for himself.

Gareth, who had been drowsing on top of Jason's pillow, uncurled and climbed onto the boy's lap. Jason stroked the cat and ran his finger over Gareth's only white spot—on his chest, a T-shaped mark with a loop over the crossbar.

"Lucky Gareth," Jason sighed, lying back and closing his eyes, "I wish *I* had nine lives."

The cat stopped purring. "I wish I did, too," he said.

Jason started up in surprise. Not because Gareth had spoken. Jason had always been sure he could if he wanted to. It was what Gareth had said.

"You mean you really don't have nine lives?" Jason asked, disappointed.

"I'm afraid not," said the cat, in a very matter-of-fact way. "But, since you mention it, I'll tell you a secret. I only have one life. With a difference: I can visit."

"Visit?" Jason said.

"Yes," Gareth went on, "I can visit nine different lives. Anywhere, any time, any country, any century."

"Oh, Gareth!" Jason clapped his hands. "Can all cats do that?"

"Where do you think cats go when you're looking all over and can't find them?" Gareth replied. "And have you ever noticed a cat suddenly appear in a room when you were sure the room was empty? Or disappear, and you can't imagine where he went?"

"And you've actually gone to a lot of different countries?" Jason asked.

"No, not yet," Gareth said. "I've been waiting for—oh, I don't know, a special occasion, you might say. I never saw much sense in just going as a tourist. It's better to wait until there's some important reason."

"I guess you're right," Jason nodded. He looked over at Gareth. "I was wondering if you thought there might be a special occasion coming up soon?"

"There might be," said Gareth.

"Gareth, listen," Jason said eagerly, "if it were a special occasion and somebody else, somebody you liked, wanted very much to go, could you take him with you?"

Gareth did not answer immediately. He began looking like an owl and stayed that way for a while. Finally, he said, "Yes, I suppose I could."

"Would you take me?"

Gareth was silent again. "I could take you with me," he said, after a moment, "but I have to warn you of this. You'd be on your own, you wouldn't have any kind of protection. Neither of us would. Naturally, I'd help you every way I could; we'd be able to talk to each other, but only when no one else was around. Aside from that, what happens, happens. And you couldn't change your mind in the middle.

"Oh, there's something else. Whatever you did, you wouldn't dare be separated from me for any length of time. Otherwise, you'd never see home again. Now, if you accept the conditions . . ."

"Oh, Gareth, I accept!"

"Are you sure?" the cat asked. "Think carefully."

Jason nodded.

"Very well," said the cat. "Look into my eyes." And he gave Jason a long, slow wink.

The Adventure Begins

by Pierre Berton

Penny, Pamela, Patsy, and Peter put Earless Osdick, the cat, and Pollywog, the baby, into the Playhouse for safekeeping and went off. While they were gone, a little green man pulled the cat down into a hole in the floor, and Pollywog followed. When the children returned and found the Playhouse empty, Pamela remembered seeing a little man saw a trapdoor in the floor. Hooking his tractor to a nail head, with a piece of string, Peter slowly opened the trapdoor in the Playhouse floor.

All four got down on their knees and stared into the black hole that had opened up beneath the Playhouse.

"Polly?" shouted Penny. "Polly? Are you down there?"

No answer. Not even an echo.

from The Secret World of Og

"Woof! Woof!" barked Patsy. She did it extremely well but there was still no answer.

"Penny, get a rock and drop it down," Pamela suggested. "We can tell how far down it is when we hear it land."

"*I* will!" squealed Patsy. She rushed out the door and returned in an instant, with several rocks of various sizes. She dropped one in and heard it make a satisfying PLOP almost at once.

"It can't be very far to the bottom," Penny said. "Pete, drop your tractor down on the string and see if you can feel anything."

Peter unhooked his tractor from the nail on the trapdoor and suspended it into the gloom, reaching as far down as he could.

"Touched something," he said.

"Pull it up!"

Peter hauled the tractor up. It had sand on its wheels.

"It can't be very far down," said Penny.

"Somebody's going to have to go down there," said Pamela a little uncertainly.

"I will! I will!" squealed Patsy, who was known in the family as The Volunteer. She had clambered halfway into the darkness when Penny pulled her back.

"No you *won't*, Patsy," she said firmly. "It's up to me."

It took a great deal of courage for Penny to say this, for she was mortally afraid of what lay below. Pamela's story of the mysterious trapdoor and the strange little man who was colored green, the Pollywog's absolute disappearance, the darkness and the mystery—all these things terrified her.

She was so scared she was trembling but all the same she knew she must go for she was the oldest and she was the one responsible for Paul. She would have to set an example to the other children who instinctively followed her lead. If anybody else was going to get swallowed up or captured by

80

Green People, then she would have to be the one. If she did not take the lead now, she knew she would be sorry for it all her life.

"Yes—come on back, Patsy," said Pamela, understanding everything clearly. "Penny has to go."

Penny swung herself over the side of the pit, holding on to the edge of the Playhouse floor with her hands. For a moment she clung there, a thin frightened little girl in an old discarded evening dress, holding her lips tightly together to keep her teeth from chattering. Then she let go and the other children could hear a KLUMPH! as she hit the bottom.

"Are you all right, Penny?" Pamela called down.

"I think so," came the answer. "It's sort of sandy. I'm going to feel around."

They could hear her moving around below, in the darkness, and then they heard her voice, hollow in the gloom, call upward again in excitement.

"There are little steps here! They go down! I'm going to follow them down . . ."

"Wait, Penny," Pamela called. "We'll all come. It'll be a lot safer."

She could almost hear Penny thinking about this in the dark below.

"All right, then," Penny said, for she desperately wanted company. "Let the little ones down first and you bring up the rear." It was a phrase taken from *Lucy Lawless, Girl Pirate:* "Let the prisoners go first, Cap'n, and you bring up the rear."

"Maybe we ought to take Yukon King," Patsy said. "He's never had a real adventure. It would do him good."

"He could *pertect* us," Peter said soberly. He was the only one, besides Yukon King, who really believed in Yukon King's invincibility.

"I don't s'pose it would hurt," said Pamela.

"I'll get him!" Patsy squealed and rushed off to the big elm tree where Yukon King could always be found asleep on a hot afternoon.

"Wait, Penny," Pamela called. "We're going to bring Yukie."

Yukon King (who very much disliked being called "Yukie") was at that moment lying flat on his back with his tiny paws in the air, snarling in his sleep. He was redreaming an episode from Corporal Clancy of the Klondike, which he had seen on TV the previous Monday. He had just reached the part where Corporal Clancy, bound hand and foot by The Bonanza Bandit, is saved by his faithful and incredibly intelligent malamute (played by Yukon King). Then Patsy woke him up by rolling him over.

Yukon King bounded high into the air, and, with his back to the tree, bared his teeth, preparing to meet all comers. Then he saw Patsy, dropped the role of malamute, and crawled up to her, wiggling his little behind.

"C'mon, Yukon King," said Patsy, being careful to address him formally because of the importance of the occasion. "We're going on an adventure and you're going to protect us."

The effect of this speech on the little dog was electric. He puffed out his tiny chest, raised his head in the air, and began to strut toward the Playhouse, fairly bursting with pride. Patsy had been right. An adventure—*any* adventure—would do him good.

"We'd best drop him down first," said Pamela, as the two arrived back. She picked up Yukon King and held him over the abyss. He didn't like it a bit and was about to yelp in terror, but thought better of it. If

he showed fear they mightn't take him at all. Pamela dropped him and Penny caught him in her arms and Yukon King was so grateful to find a friend below that he slobbered all over her.

"All right, Peter, over you go," Pamela said.

"Wait," said Peter, retrieving his tractor and stuffing it in his pocket. Then he jumped down quickly and Penny caught him. Patsy came next in an enthusiastic bound. "It's so *jalopy*," she whispered to Peter and the two hugged each other with excitement and delight.

"Come on, Pam," Penny called. But Pamela was not to be hurried. Very slowly and very methodically she closed the Playhouse door. She looked about and picked up as many of the little boxes of candies as the pockets of her shorts would hold. Then she carefully slung herself over the edge and dropped down.

The adventure had begun.

Bits, Bytes, Chips, and Blips

Spring gling
flingle jingle
jing wring
sing wing
bring ting
ring ding
dingle ding
ding a ling
ling a ring
ring ring
jing a ring
wing a ling
spring a ling
spring swing
wing ing
fling spring
sprang spring
SPR . . . . . . ING!
SPRING

— *"The Computer's Spring Greeting"*
by Gary Lewis

Computer keeps boy in touch with school

Reprinted with permission—*The Toronto Star* Syndicate

Stacey Slater and his mom, Debbi, try out the computer that will keep Stacey in touch with his classmates and school studies. Heart disease prohibits the twelve-year-old from attending school.

The Toronto Star
February 19, 1987

By Virginia Corner

Twelve-year-old Stacey Slater can no longer go to school because of major heart problems.

But he'll soon be closer than ever to his teacher and classmates.

In a unique attempt to meet Stacey's special needs, North York Board of Education is hooking up a computer in his home with a computer in the grade 6 class at Summit Heights Public School.

It's the first time the board has tried to connect a student to his classroom when he can't physically be there. Stacey will be able to communicate with his peers and follow what's being taught in school without leaving his Sandringham Dr. home.

And there are other benefits for Stacey, who is excited about the prospect. "This way I'll be able to speak to my friends almost every day," he says. "It will also be nice to talk to my teacher. And to get all the gossip from everybody."

Four years ago, it became clear that Stacey, who is highly prone to infection, could not return to school. A home instruction teacher began coming to the house three hours a week. Janet Batchelor is now at the Slater home seven and a half hours a week.

Debbi Slater and her husband, Ken, approached the North York Board of Education about a computer for Stacey.

"We felt that there was an opportunity here, not only to serve his needs, but to serve some needs of other students," says Ron Mason, the board's special education co-ordinator. "We want students to have the opportunity to grow up together. It would be not only good for Stacey but for his classmates to be able to know one another a little better."

The cost of setting up the matching computers will be well under $10 000, Mason says.

"I am thoroughly convinced that the computer is the way to go, especially if it's a child like Stacey who cannot return to school," says Batchelor.

"It gives him a permanent connection with the classroom."

Batchelor believes home instruction "can only do so much. But if there is a permanent contact with the classroom, other students can go to that computer and get in contact with Stacey at any time during the day.

"If Stacey is resting, it won't matter because the computer will accept the message and keep it stored until Stacey is able to pick that message up himself."

Stacey's mother says when he went to school he was popular and outgoing, with "tons and tons of friends." He was taken out of that stimulating environment and during the last four years, has lived his life basically by himself, with the support of his family.

The board hopes that in the future other students who are away from school for long periods of time because of illness will also benefit from such an arrangement, says Mason.

"If we can make this much quicker by learning the way to do it, we can plug something like this in very quickly," says Mason, whose department has spent about a year arranging the hook-up.

"We can possibly provide this kind of program for an extended absence for somebody who may be away for a year."

Learning is child's play on 'Noobie' the computer

The Toronto Star
April 10, 1987

By Andrea Gordon

Computers these days come in almost all shapes and sizes—but with fur, feathers, beak, and tail?

At least one computer does, and it's the creation of graphics designer Allison Druin, with help from Muppets-maker Jim Henson.

Druin, two months away from completing her Master of Science at the Massachusetts Institute of Technology, is determined to make computers more approachable and fun—especially for kids.

So eighteen months ago, she and a team of seven computer hardware, software, and puppet specialists set about making Noobie (short for "new beast"), an Apple computer disguised as a giant stuffed animal with yellow beak, big blue eyes, and lots of fur, feathers, and even fish skin.

The beast left its home at the MIT Media Lab for the first time this week to meet the nearly 1500 delegates who attended a conference at the Harbour Castle hotel on human factors in computing and graphics design.

Eventually, Druin says, she hopes the idea can be used to teach in classrooms, hospitals, or museums.

One need not know about computer commands, menus, or control buttons to use Noobie because there is no keyboard. Druin says that although she's comfortable with computers, she doesn't warm to keyboards, steel frames, and computer codes. So she turned to the world of make-believe to try to make the computer experience more inviting.

"I put together those things that make being a child special," says Druin, who at age 23 describes herself as "a graphics designer but still mostly a kid."

Computer in disguise: What you see is more than a lovable stuffed animal. It's a computer, created by graphics designer Allison Druin, with help from Muppets-maker Jim Henson. Eventually, Druin says, she hopes the idea can be used to teach in classrooms, hospitals, or museums.

Noobie is Druin's thesis and represents a new generation in learning tools for kids. The stuffed animal is built around an Apple Macintosh—the screen appears on its belly—with wiring that runs through the body instead of to a keyboard.

All the kids have to do is touch the beak, ear, or one of the furry beast's big feet and that part appears on the screen simultaneously with one of many high-tech bleeps from the built-in synthesizer.

Without using a keyboard or computer commands, they can design real or make-believe animals.

Noobie is a prototype, and Druin says she and her team want to continue developing it for at least a year until she can think about taking it to market. She wants kids to be able to adjust the size and shape of the body parts that appear and she wants to add color and animation.

A firm believer in making technology more human, Druin says watching kids respond to Noobie might also remind adults how important it is—even for them—to make high-tech less intimidating to the uninitiated.

Meet Claire Mackay

by Christel Kleitsch

Before you wrote your novel The Minerva Program, *what did you know about computers?*

Nothing, or almost nothing, except that I knew I was afraid of them. I have a fear of technology, technophobia. I am not technically oriented or naturally mechanical. I still have the problem of which way to turn the key in my front door!

Since you didn't know anything about computers, what did you do to find out about them?

I decided that the best thing for me to do was to emulate as much as possible what I was about to have my main character, Minerva, do so I went and took a course in computer programming. And I kept a diary, not just of the lessons but of my feelings as I began to learn this and that. The repeating program in the novel, *Minerva Wright is good-looking and clever,* I actually did that on a computer, you see, so I would know how Minerva felt—how proud she was, and how amazed.

Before you started to write your novel did you read any computer books?

I read whatever there was. I usually do that with every book. I research like mad, probably too much. (It's easier than writing.) I must have read 60 or 70 books and countless, maybe 100 to 150, magazine articles.

The Minerva Program is the first book you wrote on a word processor. How do you think working on a word processor has affected your writing?

That's an interesting question. I would say it's had both positive and negative effects. It certainly has removed much of the drudgery and burden of having to redo an entire draft, entire chapter, entire page because of one small revision, and I am revising all the time.

But I've noticed a couple of other things that have frightened me. There's a further distance between yourself and your work, it seems to me. There's something physical about the act of putting words directly on paper that we may lose if we start putting them on a screen instead. There is hardly any effort if you use a computer, you know. You just touch the keys and the words appear, and perhaps there is a danger that we might lose some kind of physical connection between our own creativity and the work that eventually comes out on the printed page.

You wrote your previous books on a typewriter. How is working on a computer different from working on a typewriter?

There is more physical effort in working on a typewriter, of course, but there is something else involved too. You can leave a piece of paper in a typewriter overnight, so that as you pass by you see that piece of paper, a page of your manuscript, looking at you. You are maybe stopped in the middle of a sentence, and as you pass by you maybe have an idea, and you sit down and do it. With a computer, there is a deliberate and rather complicated act of sitting down in front of the machine, turning on the switch, putting in the disks if they are not already in there, calling up the manuscript, getting to

the right page, and then doing it. A whole lot of clicks and buzzes and mechanical things and electronic things are involved before your manuscript is in front of you—and then it's in a strange form, on a screen, not in a tangible form you can hold in your hands.

And that brings up another difference. Unless you take a hard copy each time there is something less satisfying about doing a book on disk, it seems to me, because you don't see the pages pile up. I make a habit of taking a hard copy because it's comforting to me to see the pages pile up, to see the manuscript as something physical.

So when you take hard copy you have pages that look like a typewritten manuscript. Is that one way that working on a computer is the same as working on a typewriter?

No. The pages look different. Because it's possible with the delete key to make changes on the screen and because it is so easy to print out a clean page, you're tempted to get the page out there. And that's a danger. Because it's a clean page you have the sense of "oh, it's finished," when it's not finished at all. It's not the best you can do, but it looks nice and clean, so it looks like a final draft. But with a typewritten manuscript, before you even have a page out of the roller, you've penciled in this and that, you know you are going to change it, and you can see it's a first draft.

You've talked mostly about the dangers. What about the benefits of writing on a computer?

I mentioned removing the absolute drudgery of doing minor corrections which manage to shift every page in a manuscript. That certainly is a blessing, and I can speak of that with some feeling because in *One Proud Summer* I had to change several of the characters' names at the last minute. Well, you

can imagine, without a computer, what that meant. I had little bits of sticky paper all over my room, all over myself, all over the manuscript, and it was really a bad scene. In *The Minerva Program* I changed a name at the very last minute and the computer simply made the change throughout the whole manuscript.

Since it's so easy to make changes on screen, do you do most of your editing on screen or do you still do a lot of it on hard copy?

I do most of it on the screen now.

But when you read five or six chapters to get a sense of how things are going, would you read them on the screen or on hard copy to decide which chunks aren't working and need changing?

You're quite right. I might call up a chapter to read on the screen, but I would want to read five or six chapters on hard copy. At that point I might discover that hey, this doesn't quite follow and move paragraphs.

I still get a better sense of the whole book and where things are in it from hard copy. I am still that much tuned in to the physical book.

After writing your novel about kids and computers, what conclusions did you come to?

I see the computer, like any technology, as a double-edged sword. It has benefits and disadvantages, and I hope we learn the wisdom to use it properly. As far as kids and computers are concerned, I think there are dangers in the rush to stuff computers into all our schools and to turn kids on to computers at an early age. We must be careful that we don't send kids the message that information is thought, that because they can process information on their machines they are therefore thinking.

Snogel and Drogel

by Kenneth Oppel

Every day after school Colin went to a nearby delicatessen to play a video game called Meteoroids. This afternoon, just as he started to play, there was a blinding flash on the video screen and the machine broke down.

When he reached his house Colin took the door key from underneath a flat stone in the garden and went inside. In the kitchen he dumped his books on the table and made himself a snack: a glass of milk, two chocolate biscuits, and an apple. He carried all this into the living room and flopped on the sofa. He switched on the television set with the remote-control unit.

"I simply cannot believe it!" an enormously fat lady was squealing. She had just won a new car on a quiz show. "I just can't believe it! Is this wonderful thing *really* mine?"

"It certainly is, Miss Gargantua," said the host, smiling a sickeningly sweet smile.

"It's just mind-boggling!" cried the lady. She started hugging the host and giving him large, wet kisses on the cheeks.

Colin turned off the television in disgust.

As he sat there on the sofa, feeling let down because he had not been able to play a game of Meteoroids, he thought he heard faint noises in the house. It was as if two people were whispering to one another. Colin held his breath and listened harder. He heard the sounds again, this time louder. He let his

from Colin's Fantastic Video Adventure

breath out sharply. It couldn't be his parents. His mother was showing people around the area, trying to sell expensive houses, and his father was giving people legal advice in his smart office in town. Colin didn't have any brothers or sisters.

He began to get jumpy. People a lot older than Colin get jumpy when they're alone in the house and hear strange noises, so there is no reason why he shouldn't have been scared out of his skin.

In fact, he wasn't. He was quite a brave boy and was about to get off the sofa and seek out the owners of the annoying voices when he heard a distinct exclamation, which made him freeze.

"You're taking up too much room, stupid!" the voice screamed. A tingling bolt of electricity ran down Colin's neck to his feet, not because of *what* he heard (that really wasn't too alarming) but because of *where* it came from—his *shirt pocket!*

Cautiously, he lifted the flap of the pocket and looked inside to see . . . the helmeted heads of two very tiny men, and they were looking right up at Colin, their eyes wide, their mouths gaping slightly.

"Oh, *now* look what you've done," moaned one of the little men, clutching his helmet. "If only you'd been quiet."

"Shut up!" shouted the other, glaring at his companion. "This is all your fault! You were standing on my foot and your elbow was jammed into my stomach. I never should have agreed to your silly plan!"

The man clutching his helmet looked at Colin. "If you would be so kind . . . if you would be so kind as to get us out of here."

Colin nodded and carefully reached down into his pocket and brought out the two diminutive people, placing them gently on the coffee table.

Now that they were out of his pocket Colin could see them more clearly. Both were wearing what looked like spacesuits, but on their feet they wore training shoes! On their hands were black gauntlets. One of the little men was slim; the other was slightly shorter and quite stout. They took off their bubble-like helmets and held them at their sides.

"Who are you two?" Colin croaked. His mouth had gone dry so he reached for his glass of milk and took a small sip.

"I am Drogel," the taller of the two said. "And this is—"

"Snogel," interrupted the stout one.

Colin looked above their heads, searching carefully for fine strands of thread. Perhaps these little people were puppets.

"What are you doing?" Snogel asked.

"Looking for strings," Colin replied.

"Don't be idiotic," said Snogel. "We're as real as you are."

"Where did you come from?" Colin asked.

"Hmmmmm," Drogel said.

"Ahhhhh," Snogel said.

They looked at each other apprehensively for several moments. Obviously they were reluctant to answer. Then Drogel shrugged his shoulders and looked up at Colin.

The boy swallowed and prepared himself for what he was about to hear. He had a funny feeling that he was touching on the fringes of a strange, magical world.

"Well," Drogel began, chewing on his fingernails beneath his gloves, "we came from . . . er . . . we came from . . . ah . . . the game."

"How's that?"

"We came from the game, Meteoroids," repeated Snogel. "You see, we are the pilots of the spaceship." He said this proudly and thrust out his tiny chest.

"Impossible!" said Colin, absolutely flabbergasted. "It's all wires and computer chips. It's just a machine!"

"Machine, is it?" Snogel snapped. "Machine? A simple machine? My dear overgrown boy, there's more to that game than you know!"

"There certainly is," agreed Drogel, grinning. "Who do you think *really* controls the spaceship? Not you!"

Colin took a deep breath and tried to collect his thoughts. "Now look," he began slowly, "what you're telling me can't possibly be true. That ship on the television screen is

only an image! How could you fit inside a picture?"

"Ah," said Drogel, his small eyes twinkling. "That's it, isn't it! You've hit the nail on the head! What a clever lad you are. Now, if you like, I'll explain the whole thing."

"I'd like that very much," said Colin, tingling all over.

Drogel put his helmet on the coffee table and sat down on it.

"You see," he said, his voice softening as voices often do when they are about to reveal great secrets, "everything you watch on the television screen is actually happening, not inside the game itself, but on a magic level. So as soon as Snogel and I enter Meteoroids, we are whisked away into another world!"

"You mean that you and Snogel are really flying a spaceship through meteoroid fields and fighting with enemy ships!" exclaimed Colin. "Is that what you mean?"

"Exactly!" Drogel said. "What's your name, by the way?"

"Colin Filmore. And you're saying that I am only seeing a representation of what is going on in this magic level?"

"You astound me!" Drogel said.

"So I really don't do anything at all," Colin said, disappointed. "It's you two who do all the work."

"No, no," corrected Drogel. "We only do what you tell us to do with the joystick and buttons. So if you press the button that says acceleration, we speed up until you take your finger off that button. In our ship, we have a huge panel above our heads which we watch constantly. Everything you do is registered there. It's really quite simple."

"Not so simple!" shouted Snogel. "How can you say that, Drogel? It's absolutely terrifying! When you play the game, Colin, you know that it's just a game and you are enjoying yourself. In the cockpit, it's frantic. We're both watching that flashing panel above us and flipping toggle switches right, left, and centre. We get pulverized by rocks and blown to smithereens by those wretched flying saucers. One way or another, we must get smashed up well over a hundred times in a single day! There's nothing we can do about it either. Our job is simply to obey the commands of the player. I'm a bundle of nerves! And I'll tell you what's worst of all: it's when little children of five and six try to play. They haven't a clue. Some can't even reach the joystick! It's a massacre then, I can tell you!"

Drogel looked at his companion in awe.

"That was very impressive, Snogel. I love it when you get angry!"

"Thank you, Drogel."

"To be perfectly honest," Drogel said to Colin, "it is rather hectic, and that's why we left the game. We're in need of a good holiday."

"Holiday!" exclaimed Colin.

"Yes, of course," said Drogel indignantly. "We have to take rests, you know. We're people, too! Besides, Snogel was on the verge of having a nervous breakdown."

"And look what's happened," Snogel complained, pointing at Colin. "Now we've been discovered by a young brat just because you wanted to hitch a lift instead of walking. We could have been at the seaside by now."

"The sea?" Colin said.

"Yes," said Drogel. "I hear it's very pleasant in April."

"Look," said Colin, "slow down. How did you get out of the game and into my shirt pocket?"

"First of all," Drogel explained, "there are two exits from the magic level. One is through the television screen, the other is through a small concealed door at the back of the game. In our cockpit, there are two special buttons. One says EXIT 1, the other says EXIT 2. When we press one of them, *whoosh,* we're out! EXIT 1 takes us right through the screen. That's the one we used with you, so we could hide in your pocket."

Colin gave Drogel a long, hard stare.

"What's wrong?" he asked.

"These things are difficult to believe," Colin replied.

Drogel shrugged. "I'm sure that in the sixteenth century people had a hard time believing Copernicus when he told them that the earth wasn't the centre of the universe. And I'm sure Eratosthenes was laughed at two thousand years ago when he discovered that the world was not flat, but round. You see, my dear Colin, there are many things people have had trouble believing."

Silence.

"Were those real people, Drogel?" Snogel asked quietly.

"Of course they were real people!"

"All right," said Colin. "I'm sorry for having doubted you, but if you came right through the screen, why didn't I see you?"

"I'll handle this one," Snogel said. "My gigantic boy, if you will remember, the screen flashed and you blinked and turned your face away. That gave us more than enough time to dive into your pocket."

"I'd forgotten," admitted Colin. "What will happen to the game now that you're gone?"

"Good heavens, you ask a lot of questions!" Drogel exclaimed. "Mr. Schmidt will call a repairman who will bring along another pair of pilots. Then the game will be back in working order."

"You mean the repairmen know about you?" Colin cried.

"And the games company," Drogel informed him. "It's a well-kept secret, though. You are the very first outside person to learn about us."

"Where in the world does the company find people like you?"

Drogel ran a gloved hand through his hair and looked at Snogel. Snogel scratched his cheek and looked back at his companion. Then there was a whispered conference.

"Haven't the foggiest idea!" announced Drogel afterwards. "I don't know where on earth we come from."

Robots Are Not Frankensteins

by Jaap Tuinman

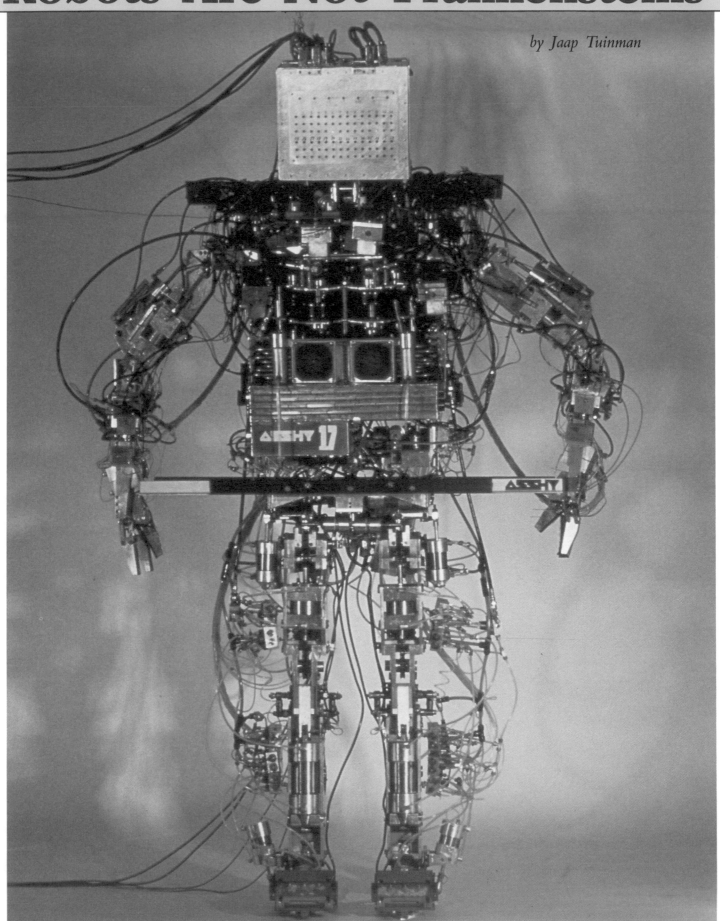

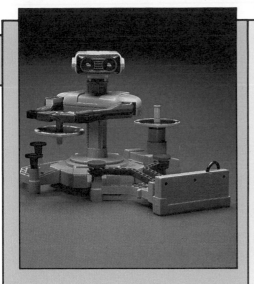

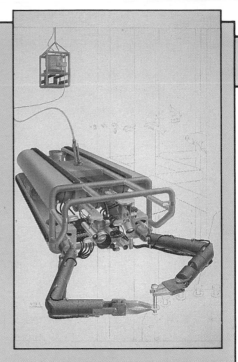

This is a robot. It is a "robotic operating buddy," R.O.B. for short, that is designed to play video games with a human partner. R.O.B. is programmed to react to coded flashes of light on the TV screen and is activated by the human player's control panel. In games where objects pop up on the screen, the player must anticipate them in time to activate the robot, which operates a joystick to zap the objects.

This is a robot too. It is mobile, it can move around, on wheels or crawler legs. The robot can move forwards, backwards, or sideways on its wheels, or it can spin around on the spot. It can crawl up stairs, and it can lift its legs, as in the photo, to step over obstacles. As a mobile robot, it can move around to do inspection and maintenance jobs like checking gauges and moving objects from one place to another.

This is also a robot. It is a *submersible,* an underwater robot. It can assemble, inspect, and repair oil rigs, cables, and other underwater equipment. Robot *subs* can dive deeper, see better, and stay underwater longer than human divers.

SO, WHAT IS A ROBOT?

"Robots are computers that can move around."

"Robots are computers with legs, arms, and eyes."

"Robots are *machines,* they do physical jobs."

"Robots are machines that think—they have computers for brains."

"Robots have memories—they can be given instructions and taught to do a task differently."

"Robots are machines that can be programmed to do a number of tasks all on their own."

AND WHY ARE THERE ROBOTS?

"Robots can work in places that are dangerous for humans."

"Robots can do the same task over and over in exactly the same way."

"Robots can do jobs that are boring and repetitious for humans."

"Robots can do physical jobs that are too heavy for humans."

"Robots can work faster and more accurately than humans can."

"Robots can work on and on without getting tired."

Robots lift, load, weld, drill, punch, assemble, paint, weigh, measure, . . .

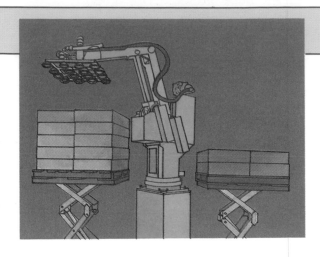

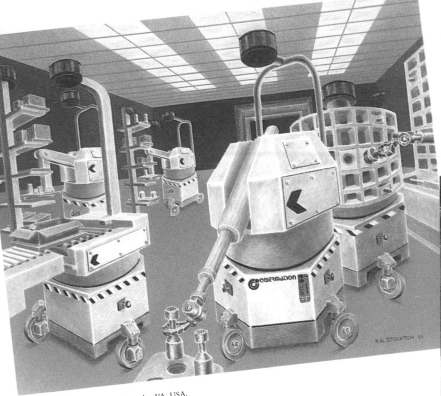

Courtesy of Cybermation, Inc., Roanoke, VA, USA.

Moving Around

Robots stay on course as they move around on their own to inspect, patrol, make safety checks, . . .

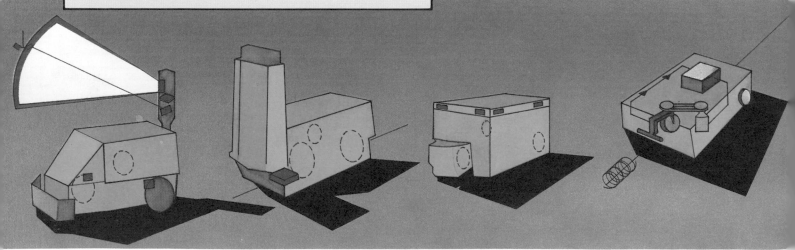

This robot uses light reflections to find its way.

This robot steers by a fluorescent line.

This robot has a movement sensor that tells it how much it's off course.

This robot steers by the magnetic field around an electrical wire.

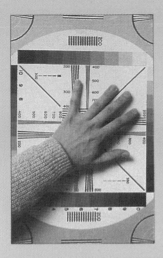
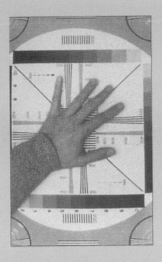
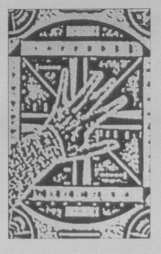

Robots don't see the way humans do. They have camera eyes that picture all the details of an object, but the computer brain can't identify which details are important and which aren't. So robots can't do what humans do: they can't recognize objects that are the same even though details may be different. Robots see pictures of different hands as pictures of different objects. They can't recognize "hand."

Robot scientists are experimenting with a machine that removes all the unimportant details that camera eyes picture so that only the essential shape remains.

Taking a First Step

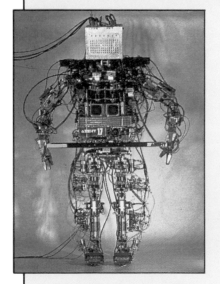

Robots can roll, wheel, crawl, or spin—but they can't walk. Except for Asshy, who can almost walk—sort of.

Asshy is 17 years old, stands 7 m tall, and has a mass of 200 kg. On a good day, with the motor in his chest pumping oil through his plastic veins, Asshy can stand on his own two feet and bend at the knee. On a really good day he may even take a step.

This is a complex steel-and-silicon-chip robot, with circuit boards in his head and two computers handling signals from the sensors in his arms and legs. And yet, after seventeen years, Asshy still hasn't learned to do something as simple as walking, which most humans can do when they're one year old.

At Home in the Future

by Ian Litterick

What do you think the world will be like towards the end of the century? Here is one view of what life might be like for Tamara and Tommy in a family that makes wide use of computer technology.

Tamara woke to the sound of pop music. "Hello, it's eight o'clock on Monday the twenty-third of February, 1999. Please get up now. Thank you."

Tamara's bedside alarm controller could switch on the light, open the curtains, and turn the radio on to play pop music.

Sometimes the music was too loud, so Tamara had been up late on Sunday night putting the finishing touches to the program she had written to make the alarm controller work under voice control.

"Shut up," she said. Obediently, the music went down. The curtains drew again and the light went off.

According to the program it should have woken her up again in ten minutes time. Unfortunately she had made a mistake in the program and it didn't wake her again. Tamara would be late for school.

But Tommy's alarm watch went off normally, so he got up.

Meanwhile Dad, who was having breakfast, got the morning report from the home computer. "It's snowing outside. The temperature is one degree below freezing. The central heating system and burglar alarm systems are working fine. There is a voicegram waiting. Thank you," it said.

Mum played back the voicegram, which was from a new client telling her that he still wanted to meet her, if she could get to his office in the snow. She pressed the remote-control button to start the car. It would need to warm up before she could take it out.

They collected the morning delivery at the door. Milk, mail, the newspaper, and the shopping they had ordered from the supermarket the night before on Teletex. (They were friendly with the delivery man, who was a computer-program author during the day.)

Dad woke Tamara up, and walked off through the snow to the local office building where he worked as an accountant for a large business. He'd play a game of squash with a friend on the office squash court before he started work. Tommy went out with him to catch the school bus.

Mum dialled up the road condition report on Teletex, flicking past the advertisements by the oil company that sponsored the report. The report told her that one road was blocked by the snow, but also told her how to get around the blockage. She tried to call her client, but his phone was busy, so she left a voicegram saying that she was coming. Then she bundled her big work computer in its attaché case into the car and set off for her meeting.

She was a technical developments researcher for a number of small companies. She searched technical data bases in New York, Tokyo, and London for technical developments that her clients might want to know about, and then sent the reports to her clients.

By the time she had eaten breakfast, Tamara had missed the school bus, so she had to dial the local taxi-bus to come and pick her up. Because she was late she would miss the computer spelling game at school. Never mind, she thought, I'll be able to do it at home tonight.

She wrapped up in her coat and went out to wait for the bus, saying goodbye to the door phone as she went. "Are you the last one out?" it queried. "Yes," she replied, and the home computer switched the intruder alarm on. It knew that there should be no more movement in the house. If it detected a disturbance greater than that made by a cat it would phone Dad at the office and then phone the police.

The home computer also turned the central heating down for the day. It would turn itself up again half an hour before the family was due to arrive home. But during the day it would keep the rooms only warm enough to keep the house plants alive and to stop the pipes freezing.

Tommy came home early in the afternoon. His class had half a day for their special projects and he was doing his at home. He tapped his secret code number into the doorlock keypad, which unlocked the door and turned the intruder alarm off. "Do you want the heating on?" said the door phone as Tommy went inside.

"Of course I do, you idiot!" he said. Tommy was annoyed that he had forgotten to program it before he went out so that the heating would come on during the afternoon. He always forgot when he was going to be back early. "I don't understand. Please answer yes or no," said the door phone. "Yes," Tommy said, adding "You idiot." He knew that the computer would ignore it. Being angry with a computer didn't get him anywhere, but it made him feel better.

Tommy's special project was a report on "Computers and Food," so he was using his personal computer to look through the education library articles dealing with the subject. Then maybe he would look at a couple of data bases that his mother had told him about. He'd write his report on the computer and add some diagrams, using the computer to help draw them.

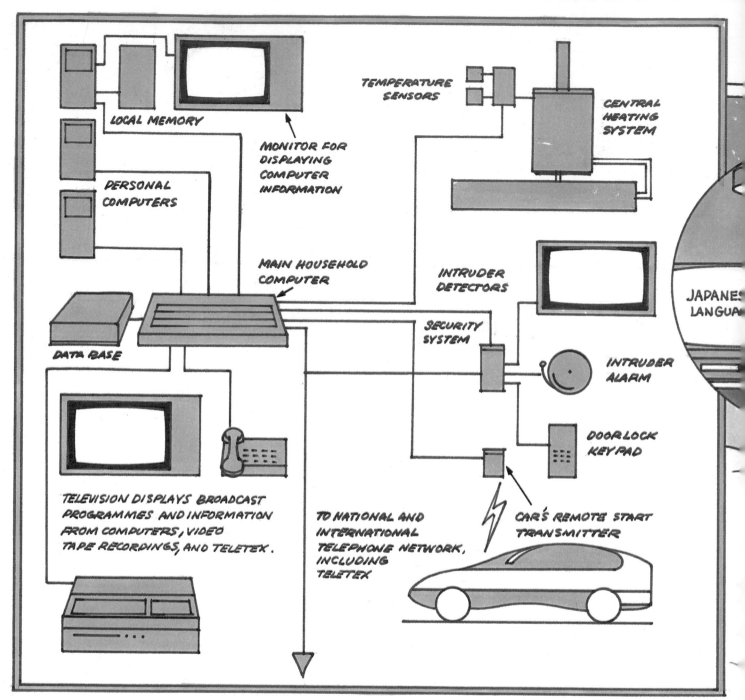

LOCAL MEMORY

TEMPERATURE SENSORS

CENTRAL HEATING SYSTEM

MONITOR FOR DISPLAYING COMPUTER INFORMATION

PERSONAL COMPUTERS

MAIN HOUSEHOLD COMPUTER

INTRUDER DETECTORS

JAPANES LANGUA

DATA BASE

SECURITY SYSTEM

INTRUDER ALARM

DOORLOCK KEYPAD

TELEVISION DISPLAYS BROADCAST PROGRAMMES AND INFORMATION FROM COMPUTERS, VIDEO TAPE RECORDINGS, AND TELETEX.

TO NATIONAL AND INTERNATIONAL TELEPHONE NETWORK, INCLUDING TELETEX

CAR'S REMOTE START TRANSMITTER

He'd made good progress this week. Last week he had spent most of the afternoon playing the new "Adventure" game he had just bought for his computer and hadn't got much work done!

That evening, after Tommy and Tamara had done their homework, the family looked through the holiday brochures on Teletex on the television set, finally booking a lakeside chalet which looked really inviting in the close-up and aerial pictures.

Then Tommy sent off a letter to his Chinese penfriend, Shiu. He sent it through the Post Office's computer translation department, which would translate it into Chinese so that his friend could read it. The letter would reach China electronically, but then be printed out and sent through the ordinary mail, as Shiu did not have a computer at home. Shiu would write his letter back to Tommy on his school computer and it, too, would be translated by the Post Office's com-

puter into English for Tommy to read.

Mum settled down with her laser-disk Japanese course. She had just started learning Japanese because she thought that it would be useful in her work. A lot of the reports that she worked on were written in Japanese. The translations were mostly done by computer and were not always very good. It would be useful to be able to check the reports in their original language.

Dad settled down to watch a film on television and went to sleep.

Tamara went back to her homemade bedside alarm system. She had to find out what had gone wrong that morning. Why had it not come back on again ten minutes after she had told it to shut up? She went to bed very late again that night.

"You'd better work tomorrow," she said to the alarm. "I'm sorry," it replied, "I do not understand." "Good night," Tamara said. "Good night," said the alarm, and obediently turned off the light. The radio would go off in half an hour, Tamara knew. That, at least, had worked last night.

The Coming of the Iron Man

by Ted Hughes
from The Iron Man

The Iron Man came to the top of the cliff. How far had he walked? Nobody knows. Where had he come from? Nobody knows. How was he made? Nobody knows.

Taller than a house, the Iron Man stood at the top of the cliff, on the very brink, in the darkness.

The wind sang through his iron fingers. His great iron head, shaped like a dustbin but as big as a bedroom, slowly turned to the right, slowly turned to the left. His iron ears turned, this way, that way. He was hearing the sea. His eyes, like headlamps, glowed white, then red, then infrared, searching the sea. Never before had the Iron Man seen the sea.

He swayed in the strong wind that pressed against his back. He swayed forward, on the brink of the high cliff.

And his right foot, his enormous iron right foot, lifted—up, out, into space, and the Iron Man stepped forward, off the cliff, into nothingness.

CRRRAAAASSSSSSH!

Down the cliff the Iron Man came toppling, head over heels.

CRASH!

CRASH!

CRASH!

From rock to rock, snag to snag, tumbling slowly. And as he crashed and crashed and crashed

His iron legs fell off.

His iron arms broke off, and the hands broke off the arms.

His great iron ears fell off and his eyes fell out.

His great iron head fell off.

All the separate pieces tumbled, scattered, crashing, bumping, clanging, down on to the rocky beach far below.

A few rocks tumbled with him.

Then

Silence.

Only the sound of the sea, chewing away at the edge of the rocky beach, where the bits and pieces of the Iron Man lay scattered far and wide, silent and unmoving.

Only one of the iron hands, lying beside an old, sand-logged washed-up seaman's boot, waved its fingers for a minute, like a crab on its back. Then it lay still.

While the stars went on wheeling through the sky and the wind went on tugging at the grass on the clifftop and the sea went on boiling and booming.

Nobody knew the Iron Man had fallen.

Night passed.

Just before dawn, as the darkness grew blue

and the shapes of the rocks separated from each other, two seagulls flew crying over the rocks. They landed on a patch of sand. They had two chicks in a nest on the cliff. Now they were searching for food.

One of the seagulls flew up—Aaaaaark! He had seen something. He glided low over the sharp rocks. He landed and picked something up. Something shiny, round, and hard. It was one of the Iron Man's eyes. He brought it back to his mate. They both looked at this strange thing. And the eye looked at them. It rolled from side to side looking first at one gull, then at the other. The gulls, peering at it, thought it was a strange kind of clam, peeping at them from its shell.

Then the other gull flew up, wheeled around, and landed and picked something up. Some awkward, heavy thing. The gull flew low and slowly, dragging the heavy thing. Finally, the gull dropped it beside the eye. This new thing had five legs. It moved. The gulls thought it was a strange kind of crab. They thought they had found a strange crab and a strange clam. They did not know they had found the Iron Man's eye and the Iron Man's right hand.

But as soon as the eye and the hand got together the eye looked at the hand. Its light glowed blue. The hand stood up on three fingers and its thumb, and craned its forefinger like a long nose. It felt around. It touched the eye. Gleefully it picked up the eye, and tucked it under its middle finger. The eye peered out, between the forefinger and thumb. Now the hand could see.

It looked around. Then it darted and jabbed one of the gulls with its stiffly held finger, then darted at the other and jabbed him. The two gulls flew up into the wind with a frightened cry.

Slowly then the hand crept over the stones, searching. It ran forward suddenly, grabbed something, and tugged. But the thing was stuck between two rocks. The thing was one of the Iron Man's arms. At last the hand left the arm and went scuttling hither and thither among the rocks, till it stopped, and touched something gently. This thing was the other hand. This new hand stood up and hooked its finger round the little finger of the hand with the eye, and let itself be led. Now the two hands, the seeing one leading the blind

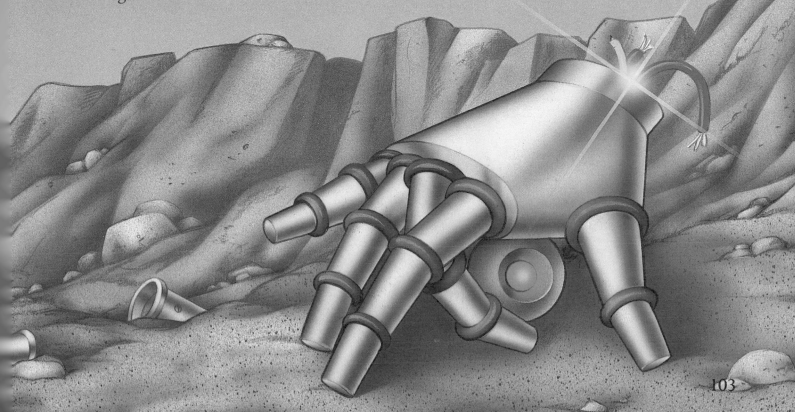

one, walking on their fingertips, went back together to the arm, and together they tugged it free. The hand with the eye fastened itself on to the wrist of the arm. The arm stood up and walked on its hand. The other hand clung on behind as before, and this strange trio went searching.

An eye! There it was, blinking at them speechlessly beside a black and white pebble. The seeing hand fitted the eye to the blind hand and now both hands could see. They went running among the rocks. Soon they found a leg. They jumped on top of the leg and the leg went hopping over the rocks with the arm swinging from the hand that clung to the top of the leg. The other hand clung on top of that hand. The two hands, with their eyes, guided the leg, twisting it this way and that, as a rider guides a horse.

Soon they found another leg and the other arm. Now each hand, with an eye under its palm and an arm dangling from its wrist, rode on a leg separately about the beach. Hop, hop, hop, they went, peering among the rocks. One found an ear and at the same moment the other found the giant torso. Then the busy hands fitted the legs to the torso, then they fitted the arms, each fitting the other, and the torso stood up with legs and arms but no head. It walked about the beach, holding its eyes up in its hands, searching for its lost head. At last, there was the head—eyeless, earless, nested in a heap of red seaweed. Now in no time the Iron Man had fitted his head back, and his eyes were in place, and everything in place except for one ear. He strode about the beach searching for his lost ear, as the sun rose over the sea and the day came.

The two gulls sat on their ledge, high on the cliff. They watched the immense man striding to and fro over the rocks below. Between them, on the nesting ledge, lay a great iron ear. The gulls could not eat it. The baby gulls could not eat it. There it lay on the high ledge.

Far below, the Iron Man searched.

At last he stopped, and looked at the sea. Was he thinking the sea had stolen his ear? Perhaps he was thinking the sea had come up, while he lay scattered, and had gone down again with his ear.

He walked towards the sea. He walked into the breakers, and there he stood for a while, the breakers bursting around his knees. Then he walked in deeper, deeper, deeper.

The gulls took off and glided down low over the great iron head that was now moving slowly out through the swell. The eyes blazed red, level with the wavetops, till a big wave covered them and foam spouted over the top of the head. The head still moved out underwater. The eyes and the top of the head appeared for a moment in a hollow of the swell. Now the eyes were green. Then the sea covered them and the head.

The gulls circled low over the line of bubbles that went on moving slowly out into the deep sea.

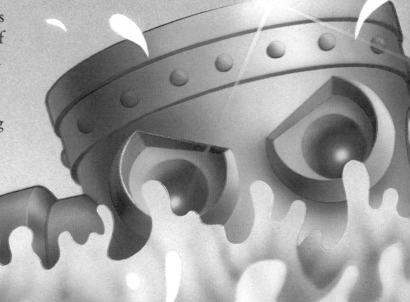

On Stage, Please

Performers take places
And lights turn down low.
Up goes the curtain
Now—on with the show!

— *by Sharon Stewart*

DANCE, DANCE, DANCE!

by Letta Ellief

Dancing is
a hop and a skip and a jump and a wiggle
and a stomp and a kick and a twirl and a jiggle

Dancing is fun
for one
or two
or four
or more

Just listen to the music
and move around the floor

Dance in a circle
Dance in a square
Dance in a conga line
All around the fair

Dance to remember
homeland
parentage
tradition
heritage

Dance to celebrate
a season
a holiday
a special time
olé!

109

Can Symphony Concerts Be Fun?

by Barbara J. Terry

Have you ever closed your eyes while watching a movie or your favorite television show? Usually you hear music in the background, and just by listening to this music, you can often tell what is happening on the screen. Even without the voices, you can guess when there is a love scene, a chase scene, or an approaching storm, and when the story gets scary or funny.

If you went to a symphony concert you would have the music, but no picture. You'd have to make your own pictures—in your mind.

Imagine yourself sitting quietly in a comfortable theatre seat. You push everything out of your mind as the music begins. What does it make you think of? Does the flute remind you of a bird? Do the drums sound like guns or thunder? Are the trumpets blasting out a victory fanfare?

To really enjoy a concert, you might want to learn more about what to listen for. There is beauty in those "toots," "oompahs," and "tweets." Don't sit there twiddling your thumbs or counting cracks in the ceiling. This can be fun!

Composers are people who write music. Many times they start with a story in mind and then write the music to fit.

Composer Bedrich Smetana wrote "The Moldau" to describe a river in Bohemia, his homeland. When you listen to it, you'll discover that the river starts out as two small streams and develops into a large waterway. Flutes and clarinets suggest the streams. Gradually, other musical instruments are added until the entire orchestra is used to create the flowing sounds of a full-grown river. As you follow the river downstream, you hear the horns of nearby hunters and the lighthearted bustle of a wedding party. Quietly, night comes, and you hear moonbeams dancing in the river's gentle ripples. Magnificent old castles rise from its banks, and the flutes and clarinets portray wood nymphs playing happily through the deserted rooms and overgrown lawns. The river encounters violent rapids before it finally, majestically, flows into the Elbe River.

Not all musical compositions are written to tell a tale, so don't panic when you hear a piece that has no story idea. There are many other ways to enjoy music.

For example, beautiful music has been written to imitate sounds that are familiar to you. There is no story to follow in "Carnival of the Animals" by Camille Saint-Saëns; instead, each short section of music describes a different animal or group of animals. You can hear a lion roar. There are violins that go "cock-a-doodle" and "hee-haw," and bass violins become elephants. Imaginary kangaroos hop from one end of the piano to the other. A flute is heard mimicking a cuckoo, and a lovely swan seems to swim gracefully to the mellow sound of a cello.

Music can also express a certain feeling or atmosphere. When Claude Debussy wrote "Clouds," he wanted to convey the feeling you get when you watch fluffy, lazy clouds drift by. Closely knitted chords (chords are musical tones sounded at the same time) are played lightly by the stringed instruments, filling the theatre. Like a cloud, you seem to drift along with the music. "Clouds" is easy to follow even though there is no leading melody.

Some composers, however, write their music around a strong melody, and in those compositions, you'll hear it soon after the music begins. Try to follow that melody! It will be repeated many times. Each time it may sound slightly different—faster, slower, higher, lower, louder, or softer. Try to find

the instruments that are playing the melody as it leaps from one section of the orchestra to another.

A symphony orchestra is made up of many musical instruments. They are grouped in families: string (violin, viola, cello, double bass), woodwind (flute, clarinet, oboe, bassoon), brass (trumpet, French horn, trombone, tuba), and percussion (kettledrum, bass drum, triangle, cymbals, bells, xylophone).

Each family of instruments has a special sound and adds its own flavor to the orchestra. Listen carefully when you hear a family of instruments play alone, as they do in Benjamin Britten's "The Young Person's Guide to the Orchestra." After the melody is introduced, each family gets to show off by playing it alone. Later, there are solos for some of the individual instruments so they can show off, too—even the kettledrums. Get to know the sounds that the families and the various instruments make, and soon you will be able to hear them even when the entire orchestra is playing.

The conductor, or person who leads the orchestra, needs the truest tone from each instrument, and the musicians work hard to achieve this. Observe how each player strives for perfection. Watch how the arms of the string players move all together. See the horns enter exactly on cue. Notice the way one percussion player uses several different instruments. One after another, they are struck or shaken at just the right time.

One of the most interesting experiences you can ever have at a concert is listening to Joseph Haydn's "Farewell Symphony." Haydn wrote the music in 1772 as a message to his employer, Prince Nicolaus Esterházy. The musicians in the orchestra Haydn directed played at the prince's summer estate, far away from their homes. They were homesick, but the prince insisted they stay and entertain him. So, during the performance of the "Farewell Symphony," each musician was given a specific time to blow out the candle on his music stand and walk off the stage. One by one they left, as the others continued to play, until only one violinist remained— still playing. The prince got the message and allowed the musicians to return home. When performing this symphony today, the players turn off their electric lights, and many of them wave at the audience as they leave. If you're in the audience, wave back!

You don't need movies or television pictures with a symphony concert. Let the music itself be the star performer, and use your mind, ears, and eyes to enjoy it!

Note: Recordings of the music presented in this article, and many other compositions for the symphony orchestra, can be checked out at most public libraries for home listening.

Show and Tell

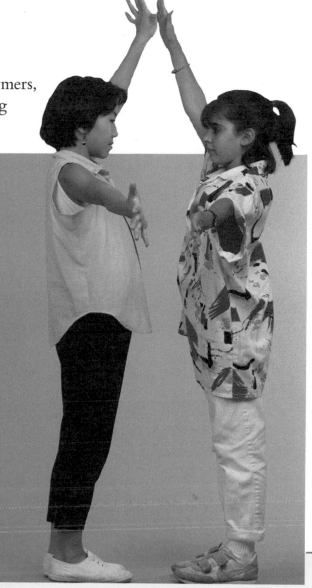

Actors, like musicians, athletes, and other performers, do warm-ups before they play. Here are some acting warm-up games.

Mirror Game: 2 Players

Face each other with your hands on each other's shoulders, then drop your arms to your sides. Decide who will be the "leader" and who will be the mirror "copycat." You can switch roles when you play the game again.

The leader slowly makes a simple movement—like raising an arm or leg, or shrugging a shoulder, or nodding. The copycat mimics the movement exactly, just like the reflection in a mirror. After a while, try a series of movements—like brushing teeth, or combing hair, or buttoning a shirt.

To make the mirror game work well
— the players look into each other's eyes as they make the movements
— the leader doesn't try to trick the "reflection" with sudden or complicated movements

Tableau Game: 3–5 Players

Think of a sport or a favorite fairy tale or story and choose a scene that you would like to present—for example, a quarterback throwing a forward pass to a receiver or Cinderella trying on the glass slipper. Try out different actions that each person could do and different ways the players could arrange themselves. When you have decided on the actions and arrangements you like best, present your scene as a tableau, or frozen picture, to others and see if they can guess what the tableau shows.

Miming a Job: 5–6 Players

Sit in a circle and try to think of a job that five or six people can work on together—like washing a car or cleaning a room.

The first person to decide on a job gets up and mimes a part of the task—hosing the car with water or dusting furniture. As soon as someone guesses what the first person is doing, that player gets up and joins in—wiping the top of the car with a dry cloth or vacuuming the rug. One by one, as they guess what the job is, the players get up and join in until you're all working together to get the job done.

As you do your part of the job, mime the actions so that the others can recognize what you're doing. What is the shape of what you're working on? How big or heavy are the tools you're using? How hard do you have to work?

Word Association Game: 10–15 Players

Sit in a circle and clap a simple rhythm, like two loud claps with your hands together and then a soft clap with your hands patting your knees—CLAP-CLAP-PAT, CLAP-CLAP-PAT, CLAP-CLAP-PAT.

In this game, you speak only on the soft beat, when the players are all patting their knees. You have to listen carefully and speak clearly so everyone can hear you.

One player says a word, any word at all, on a soft beat. The player on the left waits for the next soft beat and says a word that goes with the first word in some way, and so on around the circle. If the first player says *bottle*, the next could say *juice*, the next *apple*, the next *tree*, the next *forest*, the next *fire*, and so on. Each word goes with the word just before it, so you can end up with a word that's completely different from the one that started the game.

If you get stuck and can't think of a word that goes with the last one, say a word that rhymes—after *tree* you could say *bee* or *knee*. If you can't think of any word at all, step out of the circle while the game goes on.

Name Calling Game: 5–6 Players

The "name of the game" is to experiment with saying your names in as many different ways as you can. Here are some ideas.

Volume: Try different ways of saying some names very loudly and some very softly.

Pitch: Say some names in a high voice and some in a deep voice.

Tempo: Try different speeds, from very, very fast to really s–l–o–w.

Stress: Emphasize syllables in different ways, giving some a really sharp, strong beat and stretching out others.

Tone: Use different tones of voice to show that you're angry, sad, shy, whining, happy.

Making Machine Sounds: 4–5 Players

Use your voices to make the sounds of different machines.

What kinds of sounds would come from machines that make these things?

— robots
— ping pong balls
— teddy bears
— automobile tires
— orange juice
— pencils

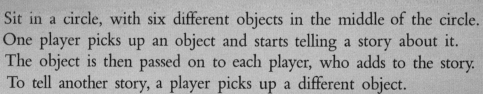

Sit in a circle, with six different objects in the middle of the circle. One player picks up an object and starts telling a story about it. The object is then passed on to each player, who adds to the story. To tell another story, a player picks up a different object.

You can also tell a circle story with each player having a different object right at the start. One player starts the story and then each of the others in turn brings his or her object into the story. Try to make your object important in your part of the story, but remember that your part must fit because you are all telling bits of the same story.

Conversation Game: 2 Players

Walk up to your partner and ask a question that gives a job clue. For example, you could ask, "May I have a ticket to Prince George, please?" or "Is my car ready yet?" Without having said "you are a railway ticket seller" or "you are a garage mechanic," you have told your partner what his or her job is. You and your partner then carry on a conversation.

Take turns asking questions with job clues to start conversations.

Jenny the Juvenile Juggler

by Dennis Lee

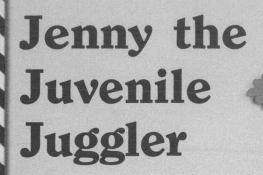

Jenny had hoops she could sling in the air
And she brought them along to the Summerhill Fair.
And a man from a carnival sideshow was there,
Who declared that he needed a juggler.

And it's
 Oops! Jenny, whoops! Jenny,
 Swing along your hoops, Jenny,
 Spin a little pattern as you go;
Because it's
 Oops! Jenny's hoops! Jenny,
 Sling a loop-the-loop, Jenny,
 Whoops! Jenny, oops! Jenny, O!

Well, the man was astonished at how the hoops flew,
And he said, "It's amazing what some kids can do!"
And now at the carnival, Act Number Two
Is Jenny the Juvenile Juggler.

And it's
 Oops! Jenny, whoops! Jenny,
 Swing along your hoops, Jenny,
 Spin a little pattern as you go;
Because it's
 Oops! Jenny's hoops! Jenny,
 Sling a loop-the-loop, Jenny,
 Whoops! Jenny, oops! Jenny, O!

How to Become a Magician

by Sid Fleischman

Introduction or
How to Vanish an Elephant

Snap your fingers. I'll wait.
Done?
I'll tell you why in a moment.

Have you ever wondered how magicians *become* magicians? After all, there are few schools for sorcery in the Yellow Pages.

Magicians teach themselves magic. But then, you have already taught yourself a lot of things: catching a ball, jumping rope, whistling, and maybe wiggling your ears.

You may start with a simple trick and someday vanish an elephant.

Magicians come in all shapes and ages. There have been famous magicians with short, plump fingers. Many are left-handed. And there are wondrous wizards no older than seven or eight.

I was ten when I first became interested in hokery-pokery. After learning a few tricks from a book, I discovered the biggest secret of all. Unless I rehearsed in private I fumbled the trick in public.

A school play would be a shambles if the actors did not first rehearse their parts. And a magician is a kind of actor playing the role of a wizard.

A wizard makes mystic passes with his hands. He utters magic words. He appears to be in command of uncanny powers. It is all pretence, of course, but that is part of the fun. Most of all, a wizard creates an atmosphere of things mysterious and surprising.

There is a kind of suspense in watching a magic trick unfold. What is going to happen? And then—behold! It happens.

That is why a magician never tells you exactly what he is going to do before he does it. It would be like telling the end of a joke first.

Did you snap your fingers a moment ago? No trick is harder to learn and most are easier!

I hope one day you will be vanishing elephants. I'll tell you how to start. First, catch one elephant . . .

117

PENNY ON THE NOSE

Did you know that you can pluck a coin from a friend's nose?

"Look! My hands are empty," you say. And they really are. Then you add, *"I'll need a penny for this trick. Ah, there's one—"*

You approach your friend and give his nose a tweak. Behold! A real penny tumbles out.

The Secret

Lift an arm and drop a penny into the sleeve of your jacket. The coin will stay there as long as you don't lower your arm below your waist.

Now you are ready to amaze everyone. Hold up both hands and show them front and back. Even spread your fingers to prove that you are hiding nothing.

As you say that you need a penny, lower your arms. With the back of your hand toward the audience, cup your fingers. The coin will silently shoot down into your hand.

Try it right now and you'll be surprised at how easy it is to catch.

Don't make a fist around the penny. Just let it lie within your slightly cupped fingers.

Raise this hand to someone's nose, twist gently, and let the penny fall. Catch it in your other hand or a glass, which makes a fine noise. And say, *"I find more pennies this way!"*

> *Trick Tip*
>
> *Don't watch your hand as it catches the coin from your sleeve. People will look where you look, and that would spoil the trick.*

118

THE FOOL ME, FOOL YOU TRICK

"In this trick," you say, *"either you will fool me, I will fool you—or maybe we'll fool each other."*

Two decks of cards are used. Your friend selects a card from one pack. You choose a card from the other.

Your friend places his card under his shoe. You place your card under your shoe.

They turn out to be the same cards!

The Secret

Beforehand, arrange one deck with all the red cards on the bottom and the blacks on top. That will be *your* deck, the one you handle. The other—your friend's deck—is untouched.

Spread your deck and have a card selected. If it is taken from the top half you know that it is black. *"Look at it and remember it,"* you say.

Then lift off more than half the pack, have the card returned, and drop the balance of the deck on top of it. That places the black card in the red half of the deck.

Of course, if the card was chosen from the lower portion of the deck (red), be sure to replace it in the upper (black) portion.

Square up the deck and place it aside.

Offer your friend the other deck. *"Now you have me take a card."* Choose any card, look at it, and replace it. But don't bother to remember it. This is just for appearances.

Here's where the simple trickery comes in. *"Find the card in your deck that you selected from mine. Don't let me see it. Place it under your shoe. I'll find my card and do the same thing."*

But what you look for in your deck is your friend's card—the one in the wrong color section. Draw it out and put your foot on it. Your friend is picking from his own deck the card he picked in yours.

"So far we're even. Each of us is standing on the card we chose. Now if you should change your card to mine, I'd be fooled. And if I could change mine to yours, you'd be fooled. Right? Do you know any magic words? Let's each say one."

Utter incantations.

"Now let's turn over our cards." Let your friend turn up the card first. Then flip over yours. Of course, they are the same.

> *Trick Tip*
>
> *Sometimes a card will be selected from near the centre of the deck and you won't be sure whether it is red or black. Here's what to do. Once you have divided the deck into reds and blacks, mark the top card of the lower packet. Do this on two opposite corners with a fine pencil point. You'll be able to spot it easily, no matter how faint it is, as you spread the cards and ask that one be selected.*

CIRCUS MAGIC

by Nicole Bédard

A mysterious mist billows across the stage. Spotlights beam through the swirling clouds and sparkle off a revolving mirror ball. Masked performers appear silently out of the mist, each one carrying an open umbrella. The dramatic opening of a show in a theatre? No. The beginning of a performance by Le Cirque du Soleil, in a blue-and-yellow-striped circus tent.

A performance of Le Cirque du Soleil is different from a traditional circus show under the big top. There are no tigers leaping through flaming hoops, no elephants balancing on one leg, no dancing bears, no prancing horses—no animal acts at all. There are no brass bands playing oompahpah music, no drumrolls announcing daredevil stunts. And the circus acts aren't performed like a three-ring circus show with different acts going on at the same time. The acts are presented like a smoothly arranged stage performance in a theatre, with special effects, mood lighting, and jazzy music played on electronic instruments, including seven synthesizers.

Le Cirque du Soleil is a mix of circus and theatre. The style and staging come from the theatre, but the acts come from the traditional circus. There are zany clown acts featuring a springy symphony orchestra conductor, a performing robot, a mechanical dog show, and a clown balancing sixteen chairs. There are tightrope artists who dance and skip rope, and do backflips on a highwire. There are acrobats who spin a long rope with an open bowl of water on each end, toss it into the air while doing backflips and somersaults, and bounce it around—with their feet! And there are fire-breathers and stilt-walkers and trapeze artists and jugglers (one juggles balls out of

121

his mouth!) and acrobats who do incredible balancing acts, like building a nine-person pyramid on a bicycle.

Where did the idea for this mix of circus and theatre come from? How did Le Cirque du Soleil get started? It all began in 1981, with a group of mimes, stilt-walkers, fire-eaters, and jugglers who performed on the streets of Baie St-Paul in Quebec. A year later they organized a festival of street performers, and in 1984 they formed a circus troupe called Le Cirque du Soleil and toured the province of Quebec.

Since 1984 Le Cirque du Soleil has toured across Canada and achieved international acclaim. They were chosen to be the opening show at the Canada Pavilion at Expo 86 in Vancouver, and they won the bronze medal at an international circus competition in Paris in 1987. International circus acts from France, China, Poland, and other countries have chosen to perform as guest artists with Le Cirque. Not bad for a young circus that was formed only in 1984!

Most of Le Cirque's troupe of performers are young (the youngest is only nine years old)

and many were trained at L'École Nationale de Cirque in Montreal, a circus school for children and adults. The school, which was founded by the artistic director of Le Cirque du Soleil, teaches a mix of circus and theatre skills—juggling, acrobatics, tightrope walking . . . and also acting and dancing.

The mix of circus and theatre training may explain the style and skill of the performers, but where does the magic of the performance come from? How do the performers weave a magic that reaches out and draws the audience into a world of wonder and enchantment? Perhaps the secret of the magic lies in how Le Cirque du Soleil began—a group of artists performing on the streets, close to the people. As the ringmaster says: "In Le Cirque there are absolutely no borders—you go where you want to go and the audience follows. Our experiences as street performers give us a different spirit—an ability to reach out to people."

Dreamers and Doers

Hold fast your dreams!
Within your heart
Keep one still, secret spot
Where dreams may go,
And sheltered so,
May thrive and grow—
Where doubt and fear are not.
Oh, keep a place apart
Within your heart,
For little dreams to go.

—by Louise Driscoll

i am the running girl

by Arnold Adoff

my name is rhonda

    and i am the youngest
of three sisters
poppa plays tennis

    and my sisters swim
and jog and walk
but
  i am the running girl
    in the family

    momma used to run

    when she was in school
      in this town

    now i am following

each morning early
    before school

momma is on the bike
and i am in my running
    shoes
along the sidewalks
  of this
    side
  of town

in my head
    i am the panther on the plain

in my head
    i am the fox in the field
in my head
    i am faster
than the animals

pushing
  against
the
air

after a while
        there is no momma or bike
or my moving
        legs

i am only two feet banging
        onto the concrete
            and blacktop
               streets
of this early morning
        run

and i am tired to my toes
        when we get home

last year i was a sprinter
           and ran short dashes
and didn't know how far
        i could go

then this winter my legs began to grow
and i became stronger
        and i could run
           long
        distances
and race a longer
        time
        around the track
        past the place
where it would begin
        to hurt

after

afternoons of running over country roads
and jogging around the track
to practise
        running form
        for hours
one
day it is april and we must be ready
        for the season
        to begin
i am ready

at the meet i must warm up slowly

        with jumping jack exercises
        and jogs around the track

        i have to loosen my legs
        and tighten my mind
        and think
about
    the
    run

just before my race

i say hello
to the other
              girls
and
sip some orange
              juice
and
  water

we smile
        and lie
        a little
about
    experience
and
    time
and
    line up
        in our l a n e s
waiting for the gun

880

        get a good start and stay
        in the pack
                  around the first
                            turn
        and stay with the
                      leader
        after the first
                  time
                  around the track

        and stay with the leader
        until it's time to try
                    and get ahead
        until it's time to
                    kick

thinking to kick

when i am running right
and the
            long muscles
of my legs are
                      moving
long and loose
              and my head is tight
                    into the race

and the first time around
              was fast enough to keep up
              but not too fast
                            to make me
use up all
          my strength

i am near the shoulder
        of the girl
        in the lead

and maybe this lead girl
        looks
          back
for a second
to see if i am still
    on her shoulder

then my eyes
tell her
    good
      bye

kick

i can switch to my fastest speed
because i can press that button
             in
      my brain

and the power of orange juice
and candy bars
        and morning runs
          with momma
slides down my throat
        and stomach
        to
        my legs

and i can pump and pump
around
    the final turn
      to the tape

home

the other girls
      fall far   behind
      like a dream story

and the lead girl is moving
  in her place
  is standing
      still

i open my legs wide and stride once
        for her two steps

i am making the breeze
i am
   the breeze

i am the race

the end

　　is past the tape at the finish line
　　and i am bending to the ground
　　　　　out of breath
　　　　　and strength

　　the coach is shouting
　　　　　i have broken　three
　　　　　　　minutes
　　for the first time
　　but i am out of
　　　　　time

　　　i have no bones
　　　i have no legs
　　　i have no
　　　　　stomach that will stay
　　　　　　where it began
　　but i have won

after the race

　　　　　my friends hug me
　　the way i hug them after their
　　　　　　races

　　while i am running they are all
　　　　a blur of faces
　　　　　　　as i come around
　　　　　　　　the turns

　　but
　　now there is my sister
　　　　there is my father
　　and
　　my momma taking
　　　　　　pictures
　　of my dirty
　　　　face

i am the running girl

　　　　there are walking girls
　　　　　and jogging
　　girls
　　　　in the streets

　　girls who ride their
　　　　　　bikes
　　and hike along brown
　　country roads with
　　　　　brothers
　　and their friends
　　and pull wild flowers
　　　　for their hair
　　but

i am the running girl
　　　　there in the moving day
　　　　and i cannot stop to
　　　　　　say
　　hello

The Boy Who Came with Cartier

by Chip Young

"There was a time, however, a long time ago,
when I lived in the Old Country.
I was young in those days, and
I wanted to see the New World.
It was as simple as that.
I left home, displaced by dreams.

"I went to the waterfront, and there she was:
a small wooden ship with colors flying.
Bound for the New World, they told me.
I had no money, so I slipped aboard,
a stowaway with only the clothes on my back,
and a loaf of bread.

"Three days I hid between the decks,
wide awake so the rats would see my eyes
and keep their distance.
('Don't close your eyes, or the rats
will pick your pockets,' an old sailor had once told me.)

"On the fourth day I must have fallen asleep,
because suddenly the bread was gone.
But we were at sea and there was no turning back.
I prayed the captain wouldn't throw me overboard,
or tie me to the mast,
as I crawled up to daylight.

"The captain, a giant of a man with pointed whiskers,
only laughed and ordered me filled with bread and salted pork,
and a cup of wine.
Mind you, I earned my passage
before that voyage was done.
A hundred times I scrubbed the galley, pots and kettles,
and wished I'd stayed at home.

"But in the end,
when I first glimpsed the world that I had come to see—
a world white men had never seen before (or so the captain said)—
I felt that I had fallen on my feet.
For the world that I saw looked as it must have done
that first morning in Genesis,
in the Beginning, before Man came.
Tall trees and grass, low mountains and plains—
new and fresh and clean.
My father at home had read of such things to me
from the Bible, after supper.

"The anchor was dropped;
a boat was lowered; and the captain pulled ashore,
to place, high up among the rocks,
a wooden cross
and claim the land for King and France.
That was long ago, so long ago that only
dreams and history books can take you there.

"When the time came to set the sails for home
I had to choose: To go? To stay?
The tide was full.
I told them, then,
'My place is here—or so it seems to me.'
They sailed away but I remained,
alone, to face the wilderness.

"It wasn't a Country.
Just trees and grass, and hills and mountains,
with lakes and rivers between.
Nothing else, except here and there a friendly fire
among the wigwams on the shore.
Native houses, the captain had said. Indians.
But they were friendly, and there was land enough for all.

"Right away I had to think about the weather;
the nights were cold.
So I cut down trees, enough to build a shelter.
And, where there was room between the stumps,
planted seeds of yellow grain
which the Indians gave to me.
The seed grew tall and strong,
and when the harvest came, we shared.

"The ship came back.
A hundred ships. A thousand men,
some with wives and children. A welcome sight!
More trees came down. A trail was made. More cabins,
and more clearings where the grain would grow.

"The snow was deep. The floods were deeper.
The cold was like a stinging pain.
The heat was sticky.
Flies. Mosquitoes. Mud, and rocks.
There were times when I cried out in the lonely darkness,
'How much can a man take?'
The answer was always there in the land,
And in the Book my father had read to me at home:
A man can take as much as he can dream.

"Every day there were a hundred reasons
why I should have left it all and sailed away.
But I stayed,
too stubborn to admit I couldn't call it home.

"Fever and sickness, cheap money and high prices;
they almost got the best of me at times.
But I stayed until the land was truly home.
Until I was as native as the rocks and trees,
the snow and flies—mosquitoes, too.

"More ships. More people.
More settlers coming up the road.
More trees falling; more brush smoke.
Cabins in the clearings, lilacs by the door.
The sound of children's laughter and the ringing of an axe.
The wilderness was giving way to those who dared to dream."

Troy: City of Legend

by Roy A. Gallant

AND CITY OF SPLENDOR

When he was a child leafing through his books on ancient history, Heinrich Schliemann promised himself that he would one day visit the city of Troy. Most scholars of the time looked on Troy as a mythical city, invented by the bards of old for the purposes of entertainment. The poet Homer's detailed accounts of the heroes of the ten-year war between the Greeks and the Trojans, often sung at feasts in ancient Greece, had held the boy spellbound. In his long poem, the *Iliad,* written almost 3000 years before young Heinrich's time, Homer had vividly described gods who changed themselves into earthly forms and hero warriors dressed in golden armor, riding chariots drawn by horses with supernatural powers.

He also described how the Greeks finally managed to defeat the Trojans safely secured within the high and solid stone walls surrounding their city. Realizing that they could not break through those walls, the Greeks had built a huge, hollow wooden horse. One night their best warriors had climbed into the horse and closed the secret entrance. The rest of the Greeks had then departed, pretending to give up the battle and leaving the horse as a "gift" to the Trojans. In the morning the Trojans saw the horse and were delighted with the gift. They opened the gates to their city and with great difficulty dragged the wooden horse with its deadly cargo inside. An evening of gaiety in celebration of the departure of the Greeks followed. But later that night, as the Trojans slept, the Greek warriors climbed out of the horse and attacked Troy, ending the Trojan War at last.

How Heinrich wanted to travel to Troy, to stand on the ground where the blood of Homer's heroes had been spilled and see the city gates through which the great horse had once passed! How disappointed he was when his father explained that historians looked on the poems of Homer as fancy, not as history. But the boy's faith in Homer's account was not to be shaken.

Schliemann was poor as a youth and had to leave school for lack of money. One of his early jobs was that of a clerk in a grocery store, where he worked for very little pay from six in the morning until eleven at night. At the age of twenty-two Schliemann joined a Dutch firm that did business with Russia. When he learned that no one in the firm could speak Russian, he taught himself that language. About a year and a half later he was made the firm's agent in St. Petersburg (now called Leningrad). Soon after that he became a merchant himself and through his talents was able to amass great wealth. By the age of forty-one he was a millionaire several times over. At last, he decided, he could carry out his boyhood dream and search for the city of Troy.

WHERE TO DIG?

Those few scholars who believed that Troy had existed in fact suspected that the ancient site might lie inside a mound near the village of Bounarbashi in what is now the northwest corner of Turkey. Schliemann went there and examined the large mound. Such mounds are often the result of cities being built on top of each other over the centuries. As each new city is built on top of the former one the mound grows higher.

After arriving at Bounarbashi, Schliemann reread Homer's descriptions of Troy. According to Homer, Troy was close enough to the sea for the Greek soldiers to travel to and from it and their ships several times a day. Homer also said, in the *Iliad*, that the last fight between the Trojan warrior Hector and the Greek hero Achilles took place outside the city walls. Three times Achilles had chased Hector around the city until he caught and killed him. When Schliemann found that the landscape around the mound would have made such a chase unlikely, and that the sea was too far away from the mound for the Greek soldiers to have made several trips a day to their ships, he decided that those who thought Troy could be found here were wrong. He would look elsewhere for the site of Troy.

After carefully examining a site called Hissarlik, and again carefully rereading

135

Homer, Schliemann decided that it was here that he would dig. He felt that Hissarlik fitted Homer's description almost exactly. He hired some hundred workers and began digging in the year 1870. His plan was to dig a deep trench completely through the mound from one side to the other. Schliemann felt that since Troy was about 3000 years old it must lie very near the bottom of the mound.

Only a few metres into the trench the diggers turned up pieces of pottery and other evidence of an old civilization, but not one as old as Troy. Deeper and deeper they went week after week. Several lost cities were uncovered; each one had been built atop an older one. After three years of digging they reached the bottom of the mound, which was level with the surrounding landscape. Schliemann had dug down through what he counted as nine different cities. Each had successively been destroyed by earthquake, war, or plague, and then had been deserted. Afterward, a new city had been built on top of the crumbled remains of the old one.

Had any of those ancient cities been Troy, the Troy ruled by King Priam, Hector's father? Homer described the great wealth of the king, such as in these lines from the *Iliad* spoken by Achilles and describing Priam's preparation to buy his son's body after Achilles had killed Hector: "He opened fair lids of chests and he weighed and brought forth talents of gold, ten in all, and two shining tripods and four cauldrons, and a goblet exceeding fair, a chattel of great price, for he was exceeding fain at heart to ransom his dear son."

Schliemann felt that much of the king's treasure must have been left behind in Troy and could be found amid the rubble. He turned up hundreds of objects valuable to

THE TREASURE OF KING PRIAM?

Immediately Schliemann told his workmen to take the rest of the day off, although the digging for that day had just begun. Schliemann and his wife, Sophie, were now alone and began to dig beneath the stone wall. Later Schliemann was to write about his discovery: "In great haste I cut out the treasure with a big knife, which meant the utmost exertion, and which might have involved the most frightful danger to life, for the great wall of fortification which I had to undermine threatened to fall upon me at any moment. But the sight of so many objects, each one of which was of incalculable value, made me rash, and I did not think of danger."

Schliemann and Sophie found rings of gold, a golden head ornament, vases of silver and copper, and weapons of finely worked bronze. Schliemann was convinced that he had discovered the treasure of Priam, but he had not. In fact, he had dug right down through Troy and into a city at least a thousand years older than Troy. It was the king of that city whose treasure Schliemann had found. Archaeologists of a later time successfully identified the layer in Schliemann's trench that was the real Troy.

But what of the treasure that Schliemann did find? He secretly moved it out of Turkey and eventually brought it home to Germany, where he gave it to a Berlin museum. When World War II started the Germans hid the treasure for safekeeping deep beneath the Zoological Gardens. At the end of the war the Russians occupied that part of Berlin and the treasure vanished. To this day no one in the Western world knows what happened to Schliemann's find.

archaeologists—pottery, weapons, tools, and ornaments—but no gold objects. Two more days of digging and then he would have to pack up, Schliemann decided. But on the day he made up his mind to abandon further search, his sharp eyes caught sight of a shiny object sticking out from beneath the massive stone wall of the city. It was the edge of a copper shield. And near it was the gleam of gold.

The Girl Who Loved the Wind

by Jane Yolen

Once many years ago in a country far to the east there lived a wealthy merchant. He was a widower and had an only daughter named Danina. She was dainty and beautiful, and he loved her more than he loved all of his treasures.

Because Danina was his only child, the merchant wanted to keep her from anything that might hurt or harm her in any way, and so he decided to shut her away from the world.

When Danina was still an infant, her father brought her to a great house which he had built on the shore of the sea. On three sides of the house rose three huge walls. And on the fourth side was the sea itself.

In this lovely, lonely place Danina grew up knowing everything that was in her father's heart but nothing of the world.

In her garden grew every kind of fair fruit and flower, for so her father willed it. And on her table was every kind of fresh fish and fowl, for so her father ordered. In her room were the finest furnishings. Gaily colored books and happy music, light dancing and bright paintings, filled her days.

And the servants were instructed always to smile, never to say no, and to be cheerful all through the year. So her father wished it and so it was done. And for many years, nothing sad touched Danina in any way.

Yet one spring day, as Danina stood by her window gazing at the sea, a breeze blew salt across the waves. It whipped her hair about her face. It blew in the corners of her room. And as it moved, it whistled a haunting little tune.

Danina had never heard such a thing before. It was sad, but it was beautiful. It intrigued her. It beguiled her. It caused her to sigh and clasp her hands.

"Who are you?" asked Danina.

And the wind answered:

Who am I?
I call myself the wind.
I slap at ships and sparrows.
I sough through broken windows.
I shepherd snow and sandstorms.
I am not always kind.

"How peculiar," said Danina. "Here you merely rustle the trees and play with the leaves and calm the birds in their nests."

"*I am not always kind,*" said the wind again.

"Everyone here is always kind. Everyone here is always happy."

"*Nothing is always,*" said the wind.

"My life is always," said Danina. "Always happy."

"*But life is not always happy,*" said the wind.

"Mine is," said Danina.

"*How sad,*" whispered the wind from a corner.

"What do you mean?" asked Danina. But the wind only whirled through the window, carrying one of her silken scarves, and before she could speak again, he had blown out to sea.

Days went by, happy days. Yet sometimes in her room, Danina would try to sing the wind's song. She could not quite remember the words or recall the tune, but its strangeness haunted her.

Finally, one morning, she asked her father: "Why isn't life always happy?"

"Life *is* always happy," replied her father.

"That's what I told him," said Danina.

"Told who?" asked her father. He was suddenly frightened, frightened that someone would take his daughter away.

"The wind," said Danina.

"The wind does not talk," said her father.

"He called himself the wind," she replied.

But her father did not understand. And so when a passing fisherman found Danina's scarf far out at sea and returned it to the merchant's house, he was rewarded with a beating, for the merchant suspected that the fisherman was the one who called himself the wind.

Then one summer day, weeks later, when the sun was reflected in the petals of the flowers, Danina strolled in her garden.

Suddenly the wind leaped over the high wall and pushed and pulled at the tops of the trees. He sang his strange song, and Danina clasped her hands and sighed.

"Who are you?" she whispered.

"Who am I?" said the wind, and he sang:

Who am I?
I call myself the wind.
I've worked the sails of windmills.
I've whirled the sand in deserts.
I've wrecked ten thousand galleons.
I am not always kind.

"I knew it was you," said Danina. "But no one believed me."

And the wind danced around the garden and made the flowers bow.

He caressed the birds in the trees and played gently with the feathers on their wings.

"You say you are not always kind," said Danina. "You say you have done many unkind things. But all I see is that you are gentle and good."

"But not always," reminded the wind. *"Nothing is always."*

"Is it sad then beyond the wall?"

"Sometimes sad and sometimes happy," said the wind.

"But different each day?" said Danina.

"Very different."

"How strange," Danina said. "Here things are always the same. Always beautiful. Happy. Good."

"How sad," said the wind. *"How dull."* And he leaped over the wall and blew out into the world.

"Come back," shouted Danina, rushing to the wall. But her voice was lost against the stones.

Just then her father came into the garden. He saw his daughter standing by the wall

and crying to the top. He ran over to her.

"Who are you calling? Who has been here?" he demanded.

"The wind," said Danina, her eyes bright with memory. "He sang me his song."

"The wind does not sing," said her father. "Only men and birds sing."

"This was no bird," said his daughter.

Then, thought the father, it must have been a man. And he resolved to keep Danina from the garden.

Locked out of her garden, Danina began to wander up and down the long corridors of the house, and what once had seemed like a palace to her began to feel like a prison. Everything seemed false. The happy smiles of the servants she saw as smiles of pity for her ignorance. The gay dancing seemed to hide broken hearts. The bright paintings hid sad thoughts. And soon Danina found herself thinking of the wind at every moment, humming his song to the walls. His song about the world—sometimes happy, sometimes sad, but always full of change and challenge.

Her father, who was not cruel but merely foolish, could not keep her locked up completely. Once a day, for an hour, he allowed Danina to walk along the beach. But three maidservants walked before her. Three manservants walked behind. And the merchant himself watched from a covered chair.

One chilly day in the fall, when the tops of the waves rolled in white to the shore, Danina strolled on the beach. She pulled her cape around her for warmth. And the three maidservants before her and the three manservants behind shivered in the cold. Her father in his covered chair pulled his blanket to his chin and stared out to sea. He was cold and unhappy, but he was more afraid to leave Danina alone.

Suddenly the wind blew across the caps of the waves, tossing foam into the air.

Danina turned to welcome him, stretching out her arms. The cape billowed behind her like the wings of a giant bird.

"Who are you?" thundered Danina's father, jumping out of his chair.

The wind spun around Danina and sang:

Who am I?
I call myself the wind.
I am not always happy.
I am not always kind.

"Nonsense," roared Danina's father. "Everyone here is always happy and kind. I shall arrest you for trespassing." And he shouted, "GUARDS!"

But before the guards could come, Danina had spread her cape on the water. Then she stepped onto it, raised one corner, and waved goodbye to her father. The blowing wind filled the cape's corner like the sail of a ship.

And before Danina's father had time to call out, before he had time for one word of repentance, she was gone. And the last thing he saw was the billowing cape as Danina and the wind sailed far to the west into the ever-changing world.

Tears Are Not Enough

As every day goes by,
how can we close our eyes
until we open up our hearts?
We can learn to share
and show how much we care,
right from the moment that we start.

Seems like overnight
we see the world in a different light.
Somehow our innocence is lost.
How can we look away,
'cause every single day
we've got to help at any cost.

We can bridge the distance.
Only we can make the difference.
Don't you know that tears are not enough.
If we can pull together,
we can change the world forever.
Heaven knows that tears are not enough.

It's up to me and you
to make the dream come true.
It's time to take our message everywhere, you know.
C'est l'amour qui nous rassemble
d'ici à l'autre bout du monde.
Let's show them Canada still cares.
Oh, you know that we'll be there.

And if we should try,
together, you and I,
maybe we could understand the reasons why.
If we take (we take) a stand (a stand)
every woman, child, and man,
we can make it work.
For God sake lend a hand.

Words by Bryan Adams and Jim Vallance
French verse by Rachel Paiement

If I Could Discover One Thing

by Betsy Byars

On Tuesday I was sitting there as usual, and I don't believe I ever saw anything as green as that field was that day. The sun had turned the grass a sort of golden-green. It was like looking at the grass through sunglasses.

And I thought that if I could discover one thing in my life, I would like to discover a fabulous new color—a brand-new color that no one had ever seen before. Here's how it would be.

I would be digging in my backyard and all of a sudden, while I was just casually digging, I would get this strange exciting feeling that something exceptionally good was about to happen. I would begin to dig faster and faster, my heart pumping in my throat, my hands flashing in the soft black dirt. And suddenly I would stop and put my hands up to my eyes. Because there, in the black earth, would be a ball, a perfectly round mass of this brand-new color.

I would not be able to take it in for a moment, because I wouldn't ever have seen anything but blue and green and all, but gradually my eyes would adjust and I would see—I would be the first person in all the world to see this new color.

I would go into the house and say to my parents, "I have discovered a new color," and my parents would not be particularly interested, because there *is* no such thing as a new color, and they would be expecting me to bring out a piece of paper on which I had mixed a lot of different water colors and made just an odd color, and then slowly I would take my hand from my pocket and hold up the smooth round ball of new color.

That night I would be on the news with my discovery and the announcer would say, "Ladies and Gentlemen, if you know someone who has a color television, go there immediately, because tonight you will see, later in our program, a new color, discovered today by a young boy." And by the time I came on the television, every person in the world would be sitting in front of his set.

The announcer would say, "Now, young man, would you tell the world how you came to discover this new color."

"I was outside digging in the dirt—"

"Where was this dirt?"

"Just in my backyard. And I got a strange feeling—"

"What was this strange feeling like?"

"It was the feeling that I was about to make a new and important discovery."

"I see. Go on."

"And I dug deeper and deeper, and then I looked down into the earth and I saw—*this!*" And I would bring forth the new color, and all around the world a silence would occur. The only silence that had ever fallen upon the whole world at one time. Eskimos would pause with pieces of dried fish halfway to their mouths; Russians who had run in from the cold would stop beating the snow from their arms; fishermen would leave their nets untended. And then, together, all at once, everyone in the world would say, *"Ahhhhhhhhhhhh."*

from The Midnight Fox

Love That Book!

Bastian looked at the book.

"I wonder," he said to himself, "what's in a book while it's closed. Oh, I know it's full of letters printed on paper, but all the same, something must be happening, because as soon as I open it, there's a whole story with people I don't know yet and all kinds of adventures and deeds and battles. And sometimes there are storms at sea, or it takes you to strange cities and countries. All those things are somehow shut up in a book. Of course you have to read it to find out. But it's already there, that's the funny thing. I just wish I knew how it could be."

—from The Neverending Story
by Michael Ende

Dear Book, I Love You

by Caroline Feller Bauer

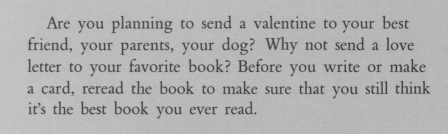

Are you planning to send a valentine to your best friend, your parents, your dog? Why not send a love letter to your favorite book? Before you write or make a card, reread the book to make sure that you still think it's the best book you ever read.

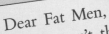

Dear Fat Men,

Why can't that happen to me? When I go to the dentist I never get a tooth that receives radio bulletins about an invasion from outer space. And I certainly have never seen fat spacemen all dressed in plaid sports jackets, knitted neckties, and two-tone shoes, running around collecting potato pancakes, pizzas, jelly doughnuts, and chocolate-covered marshmallows.

Oh well, at least because of you I can read all about it.

Thanks,
A junk food junkie

(*Fat Men from Space* by Daniel M. Pinkwater; Dodd, Mead.)

Dear Silver Pony,

Listen, next time you're flying around in the sky looking for someone to take for a ride, how about me? I do think you're wonderful, especially since your book tells a whole story without using any words.

Your friend,
Someone who has always wanted a horse
(*The Silver Pony* by Lynd Ward; Houghton Mifflin.)

146

Dear Weird and Wacky,

Thanks for showing me that other people sometimes have crazy ideas for inventions, too. It's great to browse through your pages, looking at real inventions like the dimple maker, the toothbrush for dogs and cats, and the bird diaper. I've even tried some of your inventions. (The used-gum receptacle is the best.)

Thanks for some great ideas,
A secret admirer and gum chewer

(*Weird and Wacky Inventions* by Jim Murphy; Crown.)

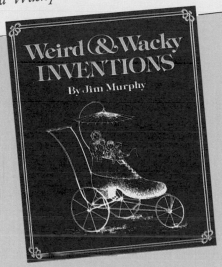

Hi! I'm Like Me,

You really are like me. There are poems in your book that think almost exactly as I do. How did you do that? One of my favorites is "Not Being Able to Sleep":

The worst thing about
Not being able to sleep
I think
Is
When suddenly you realize
That you're not going to be able
To sleep.

I'm like you,
Me

(*I'm Like Me* by Siv Widerberg; Feminist Press.)

Dear Robinson,

If you had known when you ran away from home that it would be thirty-five years before you returned, would you still have sailed out of London? I think you would have; you are a real adventurer. You made so many useful tools and discovered so many important things about your island, that you were able to survive against all odds.

You make me wish that I was shipwrecked, too.

Signed,
A captive reader

(*The Life and Adventures of Robinson Crusoe,* Daniel Defoe; Scribner's.)

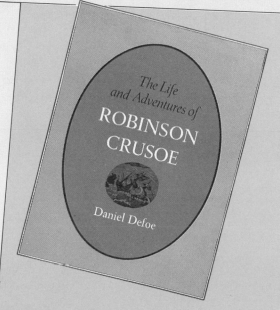

Print your letter very clearly and put it in your favorite book. You could also send it to your library—the librarian will see that your book receives it.

By Lois Simmie

Spelling

Teacher says I don't spell very well,
She says I mite even fail;
If I do I'll cry
I mite even dy
And that's the end of my tail.

Another Snake Story

I saw a snake go by today
Riding in a Chevrolet;

He was long and he was thin
And he didn't have a chin;

He had no chin, but what the heck,
He had lots and lots of neck.

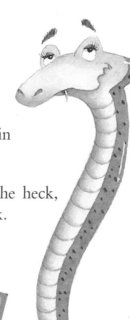

Wishing

I wish that my hair had some curly
And my clothes had some frilly and swirly;
That my nose wasn't runny
And my ears weren't funny,
That my name wasn't Alvina Shirley.

I wish that my room had some neat,
And my legs didn't have so much feet;
That my father could cook,
That my line had a hook,
That my red skirt had more than one pleat.

I wish that my cat had a tail,
I wish that my school had no fail;
That my yard had a pool
And my toad had a stool,
That my brother was locked up in jail.

I wish that my eyes were true blue
And my tooth wasn't loose when I chew;
That my bike had a chain,
That my head had a brain,

I wish I was somebody new.

Fred

My mother gave me a little plant
That was nearly almost dead,
I made up my mind to save it
And I named it Little Fred.

I fertilized and watered Fred
And talked to him a lot;
"Hi Fred!" "Whatcha doin', Fred?"
"Looks like it's going to be hot."

And Fred just sat in his little pot
On my bedroom windowsill,
Soakin' up sunshine and water and words,
Cookin' up chlorophyll.

Then one day he started to grow,
He shot out all over the place;
He grew out of bigger and bigger pots,
He grew at a terrible pace.

He grew till he filled up the window
He grew till he filled up the room,
Till he covered the dresser and closet and bed
In a sinister greeny gloom.

After I moved to another room,
We heard rustling noises in there,
And sometimes munchy and crunchy sounds . . .
I think Fred devoured my chair.

Dad said *he* wasn't scared of a plant
As he marched right through the door;
Fred rustled and munched and burped a bit,
Now Dad's not here any more.

Mom is feeling really annoyed,
She says it's an awful bother;
Nobody wants to buy a house
With a room that eats up fathers.

Now Fred is starting to push his leafy
Fingers around the door . . . .
We're packing as fast as we possibly can
And moving to Singapore.

Kids' Day at the Ex

by Bernice Thurman Hunter

I dreaded the first day of school. To me it was like the start of a ten-month jail sentence. The only thing that made it bearable was that it coincided with the coming of the "Ex." The Canadian National Exhibition was the biggest annual exposition in the world. And it was ours!

On the last day of the school year every Ontario youngster got a free pass for Kids' Day at the Ex. All summer long I worried that my free pass might somehow disappear out of the sideboard drawer and I'd be the only kid in Toronto who didn't get to go. Mum had to show it to me at least a hundred times over the summer to reassure me.

Then the day before Kids' Day I was overcome with another big worry. I was petrified I'd sleep in the next morning and miss our

free ride. So I decided to run over to Gladie's house and make her promise not to go without me.

I waited at the curb for the Canada Bread wagon to pass by. "Hi, Bessie!" I called out gaily to the familiar old brown mare. Bessie snorted and Andy, the baker, waved a greeting with his whip. From underneath the wagon I could see two feet dangling down. As it passed by, I saw that the feet belonged to Arthur. He was sitting on the step where the baker rests his basket, enjoying a free ride.

"Hookey on behind!" I squealed triumphantly.

Andy yanked on the reins and poor old Bessie stumbled to a stop. Off tumbled Arthur and away I ran, with him in hot pursuit. Gladie saw me coming and flung open the door. I streaked inside like greased lightning and just managed to slam the door in my brother's furious face.

Laughing hysterically, Gladie and I watched through the door curtains as the baker collared Arthur. Waving the whip threateningly, he gave Arthur a good tongue-lashing for hookeying on behind.

Gladie thought up a swell plan so I wouldn't sleep in the next day. "We'll make a long string," she said, "and you can tie it to your toe and throw it out your bedroom window. Then I'll come over and yank it in the morning." So we knotted a hundred bits of string together and she promised, cross her heart, not to forget to yank it.

I was scared to go home for supper because I knew Arthur would be out to get me. Of course, he would have done the same thing in my place. Hollering "hookey on behind" was a neighborhood tradition. But lucky for me I saw Willa coming down the street so I followed her in and Arthur didn't dare touch me because she was still bigger than he was.

Next morning, bright and early, Gladie ran over and pulled the string. And so did all the other kids on the street. By seven-thirty we were all bouncing merrily along Lakeshore Road in the back of Sandy Beasley's rattly old slat-sided truck. The lake rippled like a pan of gold in the sunrise. A cool wind blew across it, standing our hair on end. We looked like a bunch of dandelions gone to seed.

"*One, two, three, four, who are we for?*" sang out Buster lustily.

"*Swansea! Swansea! Rah! Rah! Rah!*" we answered.

Swansea was a separate village in those days and most of us kids were proud descendants of its earliest settlers. (Veeny Street was named after my great-aunt Veeny who was Grampa Cole's dead sister.)

We arrived at the Dufferin Gates a whole hour before they opened, so we had to sit on the curb and wait.

"I hope I don't get turned away," worried big tall Minnie Beasley. "I got no carfare home. I got to wait for Uncle Sandy."

Poor Minnie. Her parents had died suddenly of galloping consumption and she had to live with her aunt and uncle and help take care of their ten children. Mum said it was a shame the way they 'bused her.

Someone had given her a kid's ticket, but she wasn't a kid any more. She was eighteen and hadn't been to school for years.

"Let your hair down, Minnie. That'll make you look younger," suggested Willa.

Minnie unfastened her old-fashioned bun and shook a cascade of red ringlets down her back.

"Take your shoes off so you'll be shorter," I said.

"Stoop down and we'll all go through in a bunch, with you in the middle," was Buster's helpful suggestion.

It was exciting, thinking of ways to make sure Minnie didn't get turned away. It made the time go faster. Not one of us had a watch so we had no idea when the hour was up.

Our plan worked like a charm. We all surged in together and nobody questioned Minnie's ticket.

At the fountain, after deciding what time to meet to go home, we broke up into families. Grampa had given each of us a quarter. It was the most money I'd ever had in my life and I couldn't wait to spend it. The first thing I wanted to buy was a gas balloon. But Willa wouldn't let me. She pried open my fingers, took the quarter, and snapped it into her change purse.

"If you spend it now you won't have anything to look forward to all day long," she reminded me sternly. I knew she was right, but I could hardly bear to part with it.

Arthur and I always buried the hatchet on Kids' Day, no matter what. He was still mad at me for snitching to the baker, but he held my hand when Willa told him to. "We don't want to get separated and have to waste the whole day looking for each other," she said wisely.

We did the rounds of the buildings in the morning. Willa's favorite was the Flower Building so we went there first. Arthur's was the Manufacturers' Building so we went there

next. Mine was the Horse Palace and we went there last. Willa said, "Peww!" and held her nose the whole time we were in there.

Then we headed for the Pure Food Building to line up for free samples. At least, Arthur and I lined up. Willa spent her time entering contests. She must have filled out a hundred entry blanks. Win a bicycle! Win a car! Win a year's supply of groceries! Who could believe it? It seemed like a terrible waste of time to me, and she hardly got any free samples.

Arthur and I kept running back to the end of the line to get more. By the time noon hour came we were absolutely stuffed with pork and beans, soup, bologna, pickles, cheese and crackers, and I can't remember what all. We were so full we could hardly eat our cucumber sandwiches, so we saved the leftovers for supper.

The Grandstand Show took up most of the afternoon. We got in free with our Kids' Day ticket. We went in early and got wonderful seats right in the middle of the huge curved stand.

It was such a long wait in the boiling sun that Arthur finally said, "Let's go. I'm sick of waiting." And I said, "Yeah, and gimme my quarter. I wanna buy some pop and a red-hot."

"Shut up, both of you," barked Willa. "It'll be starting any minute now and it'll be worth the wait. You'll see. And I'm not missing a free show just because you two have ants in your pants."

Arthur and I nearly died laughing at our prim sister saying such a thing. And she was right, as usual. It was the most glorious show in the whole world. There were acrobats and trapeze artists, animal acts and magicians, and a man was even shot out of a cannon before our very eyes and lived to tell the tale. Then, at the end of the whole wonderful performance, came the musical ride of the Royal Canadian Mounted Police in their beautiful scarlet uniforms.

The sun was leaning far to the west by the time we got to the midway. We had no money to spend on rides, so we pressed right on through the crowd to the sideshows.

A barker stood on a wooden platform, yelling through a makeshift megaphone. "Step right up, folks . . . Step inside . . . Only twenty-five cents, a quarter of a dollar, to view all the wonders of the world!"

A huge tent billowed mysteriously behind him. Overhead flapped gaudy pictures of the hidden wonders: a two-headed baby grinned impishly from both its dimpled mouths; a bearded lady twirled her spiky, waxed mustache; and the India Rubber Man tied himself in knots beside an ugly dog-faced boy.

"Willa, Willa, give me my quarter!" I cried beseechingly.

"Don't be silly. It's a waste of money," she snapped.

"Aren't they real?" I asked, wanting desperately to believe.

"No. Only the midgets are real."

As if to prove her right, at that very moment a little tiny lady was being lifted to the stand by a great big man who leapt nimbly up beside her.

"Ladies and gentlemen, your attention please!" cried the barker, and the crowd quieted obediently. "You see before you the world's most unique mother and son. The son weighs in at two hundred pounds, the little mother at thirty-six and a half. At birth this young man was one quarter of his mother's weight. If you don't believe me, ask them for yourself."

"That's disgusting," sniffed a lady behind me.

"There's a family resemblance," said her companion.

"Hey there, fella, that really your mother?" asked a nervy red-nosed man.

"I swear by all that's holy," declared the two hundred pounder, holding up a Bible. "If I'm lying, may God strike me dead!"

The crowd glanced furtively heavenward, but nothing happened.

"Do you believe him, Willa?" asked Arthur.

"Noooo," answered Willa uncertainly.

Well, I believed him. Who but a fool or a madman would tell a big fat lie with a Bible in his hand?

After covering every inch of the midway we headed, footsore and weary, to the lakefront. Dropping down on the littered, matted brown grass, we finished up our lunch. Above us the azure sky was gaily polka-dotted with escaping gas balloons. I was glad Willa hadn't let me buy one.

"See that long cloud up there shaped like a big cigar?" said Arthur, munching on a soggy sandwich.

"Don't talk while you're eating," Willa said.

"It looks like the R-100," Arthur said, ignoring her.

"What's an R-100?" I asked, leaning back on my elbows to watch gas balloons go drifting through the cloud.

"It's a dirigible. An airship. It sailed over Toronto a couple of years ago."

"How come I didn't see it?"

"It was real early in the morning."

"How come you saw it then?"

"Because I was going to the bathroom, stupid."

"Let's go," said Willa. "It's getting late."

"I have to put Sloane's Liniment on first," said Arthur, pulling the bottle of amber liquid out of his knickers' pocket. "My growing pains are killing me."

Arthur never went to the Ex without his liniment. After giving his knees a treatment, he handed the bottle to me. "Peww!" said Willa, but she rubbed a little on her knees too. The stinging liniment felt good, soaking into our aching joints and easing the pain away.

Our second visit to the Pure Food Building was our last stop. Finally Willa relinquished our quarters. Then came the big decision. Back and forth we went from booth to booth trying to decide what to buy. Willa settled on a Neilson's bag and I followed suit. In it were six nickel chocolate bars, a pink blotter for school, a cardboard hat to wear home so everyone would know where we'd been, a sausage-shaped balloon, and a miniature can of Neilson's cocoa. Arthur spent his quarter on a Rowntree's bag just to be different. But the contents were exactly the same except our hats were shaped like a crown and his had a peak on it.

"Mine's better," I said.

"Mine is!" he retorted.

"It's six of one and half a dozen of the other," remarked our sister dryly.

Dusk was falling. One by one the colored lights blinked on as we made our weary way to the fountain. The gang gathered, a few at a time. We were too tired to talk, so we just gazed up at the pretty rainbows the fountain was spraying into the navy blue sky.

Sandy Beasley's truck was waiting for us at the gates. Scrambling over the wobbly sides, we huddled together on the splintery floor. The air seemed suddenly chilly as the truck lumbered away from the star-spangled world of the exhibition grounds.

Minnie Beasley started chanting, *"Ice cream, soda water, ginger ale, and pop. Swansea, Swansea is always on the top!"* But nobody could be bothered joining in.

Limping through the backyard of our stuck-together house, we smelled the spicy, mouth-watering aroma of simmering chili sauce escaping from the open kitchen door.

While the chili sauce was evaporating to just the right thickness, Mum was busy darning a sock stretched over a burnt-out light bulb. On the cutting board on the table, Dad was carving out a piece of rubber tire to fit the heel of his boot.

Proudly, each of us presented our mother with our miniature cans of cocoa. "Glory be!" she exclaimed appreciatively. "I'll be able to make a thumping big chocolate cake with all that lovely cocoa."

Dad put aside his work and blew up our balloons.

"Jakey can have mine," Willa said.

"Billy can have mine," Arthur said.

I kept mine and it didn't break for a week. Boy, was I glad I'd let Willa take charge of my quarter!

Rikki-Tikki-Tavi

by Rudyard Kipling

This is the story of the great war that Rikki-tikki-tavi fought single-handed, through the bathrooms of the big bungalow in Segowlee cantonment. Darzee, the tailor-bird, helped him, and Chuchundra, the musk-rat, who never comes out into the middle of the floor, but always creeps round by the wall, gave him advice; but Rikki-tikki did the real fighting.

He was a mongoose, rather like a little cat in his fur and his tail, but quite like a weasel in his head and his habits. His eyes and the end of his restless nose were pink; he could scratch himself anywhere he pleased, with any leg, front or back, that he chose to use; he could fluff up his tail till it looked like a bottle-brush, and his war cry, as he scuttled through the long grass, was: *"Rikk-tikk-tikki-tikki-tchk!"*

One day, a high summer flood washed him out of the burrow where he lived with his father and mother, and carried him, kicking and clucking, down a roadside ditch. He found a little wisp of grass floating there, and clung to it till he lost his senses. When he revived, he was lying in the hot sun on the middle of a garden path, very draggled indeed, and a small boy was saying: "Here's a dead mongoose. Let's have a funeral."

"No," said his mother, "let's take him in and dry him. Perhaps he isn't really dead."

They took him into the house, and a big man picked him up between his finger and thumb, and said he was not dead but half choked; so they wrapped him in cotton wool, and warmed him, and he opened his eyes and sneezed.

"Now," said the big man (he was an Englishman who had just moved into the bungalow), "don't frighten him, and we'll see what he'll do."

It is the hardest thing in the world to frighten a mongoose, because he is eaten up from nose to tail with curiosity. The motto of all the mongoose family is "Run and find out"; and Rikki-tikki was a true mongoose.

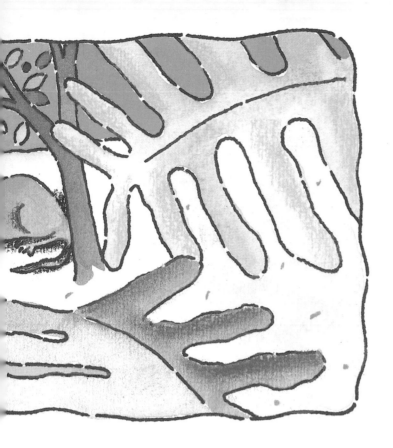

He looked at the cotton wool, decided that it was not good to eat, ran all round the table, sat up and put his fur in order, scratched himself, and jumped on the small boy's shoulder.

"Don't be frightened, Teddy," said his father. "That's his way of making friends."

"Ouch! He's tickling under my chin," said Teddy.

Rikki-tikki looked down between the boy's collar and neck, snuffed at his ear, and climbed down to the floor, where he sat rubbing his nose.

"Good gracious," said Teddy's mother, "and that's a wild creature! I suppose he's so tame because we've been kind to him."

"All mongooses are like that," said her husband. "If Teddy doesn't pick him up by the tail, or try to put him in a cage, he'll run in and out of the house all day long. Let's give him something to eat."

They gave him a little piece of raw meat. Rikki-tikki liked it immensely, and when it was finished he went out into the veranda and sat in the sunshine and fluffed up his fur to make it dry to the roots. Then he felt better.

"There are more things to find out about in this house," he said to himself, "than all my family could find out in all their lives. I shall certainly stay and find out."

He spent all that day roaming over the house. He nearly drowned himself in the bathtubs, put his nose into the ink on a writing table, and burnt it on the end of the big man's cigar, for he climbed up in the big man's lap to see how writing was done. At nightfall he ran into Teddy's nursery to watch how kerosene lamps were lighted, and when Teddy went to bed Rikki-tikki climbed up too; but he was a restless companion, because he had to get up and attend to every noise all through the night, and find out what made it. Teddy's mother and father came in, the last thing, to look at their boy, and Rikki-tikki was awake on the pillow. "I don't like that," said Teddy's mother, "he may bite the child." "He'll do no such thing," said the father. "Teddy's safer with that little beast than if he had a bloodhound to watch him. If a snake came into the nursery now—"

But Teddy's mother wouldn't think of anything so awful.

Early in the morning Rikki-tikki came to early breakfast in the veranda riding on Teddy's shoulder, and they gave him banana and some boiled egg; and he sat on all their laps one after the other, because every well-brought-up mongoose always hopes to be a house-mongoose some day and have rooms to run about in, and Rikki-tikki's mother (she used to live in the General's house at Segowlee) had carefully told Rikki what to do if ever he came across white men.

Then Rikki-tikki went out into the garden to see what was to be seen. It was a large garden, only half-cultivated, with bushes as big as summerhouses of Marshal Niel roses, lime and orange trees, clumps of bamboos, and thickets of high grass. Rikki-tikki licked his lips. "This is a splendid hunting ground," he said, and his tail grew bottle-brushy at the thought of it, and he scuttled up and down the garden, snuffing here and there till he heard very sorrowful voices in a thorn bush.

It was Darzee, the tailor-bird, and his wife. They had made a beautiful nest by pulling two big leaves together and stitching them up

the edges with fibres, and had filled the hollow with cotton and downy fluff. The nest swayed to and fro, as they sat on the rim and cried.

"What is the matter?" asked Rikki-tikki.

"We are very miserable," said Darzee. "One of our babies fell out of the nest yesterday, and Nag ate him."

"H'm!" said Rikki-tikki, "that is very sad—but I am a stranger here. Who is Nag?"

Darzee and his wife only cowered down in the nest without answering, for from the thick grass at the foot of the bush there came a low hiss—a horrid cold sound that made Rikki-tikki jump back two clear feet. Then inch by inch out of the grass rose up the head and spread hood of Nag, the big black cobra, and he was five feet long from tongue to tail. When he had lifted one-third of himself clear of the ground, he stayed balancing to and fro exactly as a dandelion-tuft balances in the wind, and he looked at Rikki-tikki with the wicked snake's eyes that never change their expression, whatever the snake may be thinking of.

"Who is Nag?" said he. "*I* am Nag. The great god Brahm put his mark upon all our people when the first cobra spread his hood to keep the sun off Brahm as he slept. Look, and be afraid!"

He spread out his hood more than ever, and Rikki-tikki saw the spectacle mark on the back of it that looks exactly like the eye part of a hook-and-eye fastening. He was afraid for the minute; but it is impossible for a mongoose to stay frightened for any length of time, and though Rikki-tikki had never met a live cobra before, his mother had fed him on dead ones, and he knew that all a grown mongoose's business in life was to fight and eat snakes. Nag knew that too, and at the bottom of his cold heart he was afraid.

"Well," said Rikki-tikki, and his tail began to fluff up again, "marks or no marks, do you think it is right for you to eat fledglings out of a nest?"

Nag was thinking to himself, and watching the least little movement in the grass behind Rikki-tikki. He knew that mongooses in the garden meant death sooner or later for him and his family, but he wanted to get Rikki-tikki off his guard. So he dropped his head a little, and put it on one side.

"Let us talk," he said. "You eat eggs. Why should not I eat birds?"

"Behind you! Look behind you!" sang Darzee.

Rikki-tikki knew better than to waste time in staring. He jumped up in the air as high as he could go, and just under him whizzed by the head of Nagaina, Nag's wicked wife. She had crept up behind him as he was talking, to make an end of him; and he heard her savage hiss as the stroke missed. He came down almost across her back, and if he had been an old mongoose he would have known that then was the time to break her back with one bite; but he was afraid of the terrible lashing return-stroke of the cobra. He bit, indeed, but did not bite long enough, and he jumped clear of the whisking tail, leaving Nagaina torn and angry.

"Wicked, wicked Darzee!" said Nag, lashing up as high as he could reach toward the nest in the thorn bush; but Darzee had built it out of reach of snakes, and it only swayed to and fro.

Rikki-tikki felt his eyes growing red and hot (when a mongoose's eyes grow red, he is angry), and he sat back on his tail and hind legs like a little kangaroo, and looked all round him, and chattered with rage. But Nag and Nagaina had disappeared into the grass. When a snake misses its stroke, it never says anything or gives any sign of what it means to do next. Rikki-tikki did not care to follow them, for he did not feel sure that he could manage two snakes at once. So he trotted off to the gravel path near the house, and sat down to think. It was a serious matter for him.

If you read the old books of natural history, you will find they say that when the mongoose fights the snake and happens to get bitten, he runs off and eats some herb that cures him. That is not true. The victory is only a matter of quickness of eye and quickness of foot,—snake's blow against mongoose's jump,—and as no eye can follow the motion of a snake's head when it strikes, that makes things much more wonderful than any magic herb. Rikki-tikki knew he was a young mongoose, and it made him all the more pleased to think that he had managed to escape a blow from behind. It gave him confidence in himself, and when Teddy came running down the path, Rikki-tikki was ready to be petted.

But just as Teddy was stooping, something flinched a little in the dust, and a tiny voice said: "Be careful. I am death!" It was Karait, the dusty brown snakeling that lies for choice on the dusty earth; and his bite is as dangerous as the cobra's. But he is so small that nobody thinks of him, and so he does the more harm to people.

Rikki-tikki's eyes grew red again, and he danced up to Karait with the peculiar rocking, swaying motion that he had inherited from his family. It looks very funny, but it is so perfectly balanced a gait that you can fly off from it at any angle you please; and in dealing with snakes this is an advantage. If Rikki-tikki had only known, he was doing a much more dangerous thing than fighting Nag, for Karait is so small, and can turn so quickly, that unless Rikki bit him close to the back of the head, he would get the return-stroke in his eye or lip. But Rikki did not know: his eyes were all red, and he rocked back and forth, looking for a good place to hold. Karait struck out. Rikki jumped sideways and tried to run in, but the wicked little dusty gray head lashed within a fraction of his shoulder, and he had to jump over the body, and the head followed his heels close.

Teddy shouted to the house: "Oh, look here! Our mongoose is killing a snake"; and Rikki-tikki heard a scream from Teddy's mother. His father ran out with a stick, but by the time he came up, Karait had lunged out once too far, and Rikki-tikki had sprung, jumped on the snake's back, dropped his head far between his forelegs, bitten as high up the back as he could get hold, and rolled away. That bite paralysed Karait, and Rikki-tikki was just going to eat him up from the tail, after the custom of his family at dinner, when he remembered that a full meal makes a slow mongoose, and if he wanted all his strength and quickness ready, he must keep himself thin.

He went away for a dust-bath under the castor-oil bushes, while Teddy's father beat the dead Karait. What is the use of that? thought Rikki-tikki. I have settled it all; and then Teddy's mother picked him up from the dust and hugged him, crying that he had saved Teddy from death, and Teddy's father said that he was a providence, and Teddy looked on with big scared eyes. Rikki-tikki was rather amused at all the fuss, which, of course, he did not understand. Teddy's mother might just as well have petted Teddy for playing in the dust. Rikki was thoroughly enjoying himself.

That night, at dinner, walking to and fro

among the wine glasses on the table, he could have stuffed himself three times over with nice things; but he remembered Nag and Nagaina, and though it was very pleasant to be patted and petted by Teddy's mother, and to sit on Teddy's shoulder, his eyes would get red from time to time, and he would go off into his long war cry of *"Rikk-tikk-tikki-tikki-tchk!"*

Teddy carried him off to bed, and insisted on Rikki-tikki sleeping under his chin. Rikki-tikki was too well bred to bite or scratch, but as soon as Teddy was asleep he went off for his nightly walk around the house, and in the dark he ran up against Chuchundra, the musk-rat, creeping round by the wall. Chuchundra is a broken-hearted little beast. He whimpers and cheeps all the night, trying to make up his mind to run into the middle of the room, but he never gets there.

"Don't kill me," said Chuchundra, almost weeping. "Rikki-tikki, don't kill me."

"Do you think a snake-killer kills musk-rats?" said Rikki-tikki scornfully.

"Those who kill snakes get killed by

snakes," said Chuchundra, more sorrowfully than ever. "And how am I to be sure that Nag won't mistake me for you some dark night?"

"There's not the least danger," said Rikki-tikki, "but Nag is in the garden, and I know you don't go there."

"My cousin Chua, the rat, told me—" said Chuchundra, and then he stopped.

"Told you what?"

"H'sh! Nag is everywhere, Rikki-tikki. You should have talked to Chua in the garden."

"I didn't—so you must tell me. Quick, Chuchundra, or I'll bite you!"

Chuchundra sat down and cried till the tears rolled off his whiskers. "I am a very poor man," he sobbed. "I never had spirit enough to run out into the middle of the room. H'sh! I mustn't tell you anything. Can't you *hear*, Rikki-tikki?"

Rikki-tikki listened. The house was as still as still, but he thought he could just catch the faintest *scratch-scratch* in the world,—a noise as faint as that of a wasp walking on a windowpane,—the dry scratch of a snake's scales on brickwork.

"That's Nag or Nagaina," he said to himself, "and he is crawling into the bathroom sluice. You're right, Chuchundra; I should have talked to Chua."

He stole off to Teddy's bathroom, but there was nothing there, and then to Teddy's mother's bathroom. At the bottom of the smooth plaster wall there was a brick pulled out to make a sluice for the bath water, and as Rikki-tikki stole in by the masonry curb where the bath is put, he heard Nag and Nagaina whispering together outside in the moonlight.

"When the house is emptied of people," said Nagaina to her husband, "*he* will have to go away, and then the garden will be our own again. Go in quietly, and remember that the big man who killed Karait is the first one to bite. Then come out and tell me, and we will hunt for Rikki-tikki together."

"But are you sure that there is anything to be gained by killing the people?" said Nag.

"Everything. When there were no people in the bungalow, did we have any mongoose in the garden? So long as the bungalow is empty, we are king and queen of the garden; and remember that as soon as our eggs in the melon-bed hatch (as they may tomorrow), our children will need room and quiet."

"I had not thought of that," said Nag. "I will go, but there is no need that we should hunt for Rikki-tikki afterward. I will kill the big man and his wife, and the child if I can, and come away quietly. Then the bungalow will be empty, and Rikki-tikki will go."

Rikki-tikki tingled all over with rage and hatred at this, and then Nag's head came through the sluice, and his five feet of cold body followed it. Angry as he was, Rikki-tikki was very frightened as he saw the size of the big cobra. Nag coiled himself up, raised his head, and looked into the bathroom in the dark, and Rikki could see his eyes glitter.

"Now, if I kill him here, Nagaina will know; and if I fight him on the open floor, the odds are in his favor. What am I to do?" said Rikki-tikki-tavi.

Nag waved to and fro, and then Rikki-tikki heard him drinking from the biggest water jar that was used to fill the bath. "That is good," said the snake. "Now, when Karait was killed, the big man had a stick. He may have that stick still, but when he comes in to bathe in the morning he will not have a stick. I shall wait here till he comes. Nagaina—do you hear me?—I shall wait here in the cool till daytime."

There was no answer from outside, so Rikki-tikki knew Nagaina had gone away. Nag coiled himself down, coil by coil, round the bulge at the bottom of the water jar, and Rikki-tikki stayed still as death. After an hour, he began to move, muscle by muscle, toward the jar. Nag was asleep, and Rikki-tikki looked at his big back, wondering which would be the best place for a good hold. "If I don't break his back at the first jump," said Rikki, "he can still fight; and if he fights—oh, Rikki!" He looked at the thickness of the neck below the hood, but that was too much for him; and a bite near the tail would only make Nag savage.

"It must be the head," he said at last, "the head above the hood; and when I am once there, I must not let go."

Then he jumped. The head was lying a little clear of the water jar, under the curve of it; and, as his teeth met, Rikki braced his back against the bulge of the red earthenware to hold down the head. This gave him just one second's purchase, and he made the most of it. Then he was battered to and fro as a rat is shaken by a dog—to and fro on the floor, up and down, and round in great circles; but his eyes were red, and he held on as the body cart-whipped over the floor, upsetting the tin dipper and the soap dish and the flesh brush, and banged against the tin side of the bath. As he held he closed his jaws tighter and tighter, for he made sure he would be banged to death, and, for the honor of his family, he preferred to be found with his teeth locked. He was dizzy, aching, and felt shaken to pieces when something went off like a thunderclap just behind him; a hot wind knocked him senseless, and red fire singed his fur. The big man had been wakened by the noise, and had fired both barrels of a shotgun into Nag just behind the hood.

Rikki-tikki held on with his eyes shut, for now he was quite sure he was dead; but the head did not move, and the big man picked him up and said: "It's the mongoose again, Alice; the little chap has saved *our* lives now." Then Teddy's mother came in with a very white face, and saw what was left of Nag, and Rikki-tikki dragged himself to Teddy's bedroom and spent half the rest of the night shaking himself tenderly to find out whether he really was broken into forty pieces, as he fancied.

When morning came he was very stiff, but well pleased with his doings. "Now I have Nagaina to settle with, and she will be worse than five Nags, and there's no knowing when the eggs she spoke of will hatch. Goodness! I must go to see Darzee," he said.

Without waiting for breakfast, Rikki-tikki ran to the thorn bush where Darzee was singing a song of triumph at the top of his voice. The news of Nag's death was all over the garden, for the sweeper had thrown the body on the rubbish heap.

"Oh, you stupid tuft of feathers!" said Rikki-tikki angrily. "Is this the time to sing?"

"Nag is dead—is dead—is dead!" sang Darzee. "The valiant Rikki-tikki caught him by the head and held fast. The big man brought the bang-stick, and Nag fell in two pieces! He will never eat my babies again."

"All that's true enough; but where's Nagaina?" said Rikki-tikki, looking carefully round him.

"Nagaina came to the bathroom sluice and called for Nag," Darzee went on, "and Nag came out on the end of a stick—the sweeper picked him up on the end of a stick and threw him upon the rubbish heap. Let us sing about the great, the red-eyed Rikki-tikki!" and Darzee filled his throat and sang.

"If I could get up to your nest, I'd roll all your babies out!" said Rikki-tikki. "You don't know when to do the right thing at the right time. You're safe enough in your nest there, but it's war for me down here. Stop singing a minute, Darzee."

"For the great, the beautiful Rikki-tikki's sake I will stop," said Darzee. "What is it, O Killer of the terrible Nag?"

"Where is Nagaina, for the third time?"

"On the rubbish heap by the stables, mourning for Nag. Great is Rikki-tikki with the white teeth."

"Bother my white teeth! Have you ever heard where she keeps her eggs?"

"In the melon-bed, on the end nearest the wall, where the sun strikes nearly all day. She hid them there weeks ago."

"And you never thought it worthwhile to tell me? The end nearest the wall, you said?"

"Rikki-tikki, you are not going to eat her eggs?"

"Not eat exactly; no. Darzee, if you have a grain of sense you will fly off to the stables and pretend that your wing is broken, and let Nagaina chase you away to this bush. I must get to the melon-bed, and if I went there now she'd see me."

Darzee was a feather-brained little fellow who could never hold more than one idea at a time in his head; and just because he knew that Nagaina's children were born in eggs like his own, he didn't think at first that it was fair to kill them. But his wife was a sensible bird, and she knew that cobra's eggs meant young cobras later on; so she flew off from the nest, and left Darzee to keep the babies warm, and continue his song about the death of Nag. Darzee was very like a man in some ways.

She fluttered in front of Nagaina by the rubbish heap, and cried out: "Oh, my wing

is broken! The boy in the house threw a stone at me and broke it." Then she fluttered more desperately than ever.

Nagaina lifted up her head and hissed: "You warned Rikki-tikki when I would have killed him. Indeed and truly, you've chosen a bad place to be lame in." And she moved toward Darzee's wife, slipping along over the dust.

"The boy broke it with a stone!" shrieked Darzee's wife.

"Well, it may be some consolation to you when you're dead to know that I shall settle accounts with the boy. My husband lies on the rubbish heap this morning, but before night the boy in the house will lie very still. What is the use of running away? I am sure to catch you. Little fool, look at me!"

Darzee's wife knew better than to do *that,* for a bird who looks at a snake's eyes gets so frightened that she cannot move. Darzee's wife fluttered on, piping sorrowfully, and never leaving the ground, and Nagaina quickened her pace.

Rikki-tikki heard them going up the path from the stables, and he raced for the end of the melon-patch near the wall. There, in the warm litter about the melons, very cunningly hidden, he found twenty-five eggs, about the size of a bantam's eggs, but with whitish skin instead of shell.

"I was not a day too soon," he said: for he could see the baby cobras curled up inside the skin, and he knew that the minute they were hatched they could each kill a man or a mongoose. He bit off the tops of the eggs as fast as he could, taking care to crush the young cobras, and turned over the litter from time to time to see whether he had missed any. At last there were only three eggs left, and Rikki-tikki began to chuckle to himself, when he heard Darzee's wife screaming:

"Rikki-tikki, I led Nagaina toward the house, and she has gone into the veranda, and—oh, come quickly—she means killing!"

Rikki-tikki smashed two eggs, and tumbled backward down the melon-bed with the third egg in his mouth, and scuttled to the veranda as hard as he could put foot to the ground. Teddy and his mother and father were there at early breakfast; but Rikki-tikki saw that they were not eating anything. They sat stone still, and their faces were white. Nagaina was coiled up on the matting by Teddy's chair, within easy striking distance of Teddy's bare leg, and she was swaying to and fro singing a song of triumph.

"Son of the big man that killed Nag," she hissed, "stay still, I am not ready yet. Wait a little. Keep very still, all you three. If you move I strike, and if you do not move I strike. Oh, foolish people, who killed my Nag!"

Teddy's eyes were fixed on his father, and all his father could do was to whisper: "Sit still, Teddy. You mustn't move. Teddy, keep still."

Then Rikki-tikki came up and cried: "Turn round, Nagaina; turn and fight!"

"All in good time," said she, without moving her eyes. "I will settle my account with *you* presently. Look at your friends, Rikki-tikki. They are still and white; they are afraid. They dare not move, and if you come a step nearer I strike."

"Look at your eggs," said Rikki-tikki, "in the melon-bed near the wall. Go and look, Nagaina."

The big snake turned half round, and saw the egg on the veranda. "Ah-h! Give it to me," she said.

Rikki-tikki put his paws one on each side of the egg, and his eyes were blood-red. "What price for a snake's egg? For a young cobra? For a young king-cobra? For the last—the very last of the brood? The ants are eating all the others down by the melon-bed."

Nagaina spun clear round, forgetting everything for the sake of the one egg; and Rikki-tikki saw Teddy's father shoot out a big hand, catch Teddy by the shoulder, and drag him across the little table with the teacups, safe and out of reach of Nagaina.

"Tricked! Tricked! Tricked! *Rikk-tck-tck!*" chuckled Rikki-tikki. "The boy is safe, and it was I—I—I that caught Nag by the hood last night in the bathroom." Then he began to jump up and down, all four feet together, his head close to the floor. "He threw me to and fro, but he could not shake me off. He was dead before the big man blew him in two. I did it. *Rikki-tikki-tck-tck!* Come then, Nagaina. Come and fight with me. You shall not be a widow long."

Nagaina saw that she had lost her chance of killing Teddy, and the egg lay between Rikki-tikki's paws. "Give me the egg, Rikki-tikki. Give me the last of my eggs, and I will go away and never come back," she said, lowering her hood.

"Yes, you will go away, and you will never come back; for you will go to the rubbish heap with Nag. Fight, widow! The big man has gone for his gun! Fight!"

Rikki-tikki was bounding all round Nagaina, keeping just out of reach of her stroke, his little eyes like hot coals. Nagaina gathered herself together, and flung out at him. Rikki-tikki jumped up and backward. Again and again and again she struck, and

each time her head came with a whack on the matting of the veranda, and she gathered herself together like a watch spring. Then Rikki-tikki danced in a circle to get behind her, and Nagaina spun round to keep her head to his head, so that the rustle of her tail on the matting sounded like dry leaves blown along by the wind.

He had forgotten the egg. It still lay on the veranda, and Nagaina came nearer and nearer to it, till at last, while Rikki-tikki was drawing breath, she caught it in her mouth, turning to the veranda steps, and flew like an arrow down the path, with Rikki-tikki behind her. When the cobra runs for her life, she goes like a whiplash flicked across a horse's neck.

Rikki-tikki knew that he must catch her, or all the trouble would begin again. She headed straight for the long grass by the thorn bush, and as he was running Rikki-tikki heard Darzee still singing his foolish little song of triumph. But Darzee's wife was wiser. She flew off her nest as Nagaina came along, and flapped her wings about Nagaina's head. If Darzee had helped they might have turned her; but Nagaina only lowered her hood and went on. Still, the instant's delay brought Rikki-tikki up to her, and as she plunged into the rat hole where she and Nag used to live, his little white teeth were clenched on her tail, and he went down with her—and very few mongooses, however wise and old they may be, care to follow a cobra into its hole. It was dark in the hole; and Rikki-tikki never knew when it might open out and give Nagaina room to turn and strike at him. He held on savagely, and stuck out his feet to act as brakes on the dark slope of the hot, moist earth.

Then the grass by the mouth of the hole

stopped waving, and Darzee said, "It is all over with Rikki-tikki! We must sing his death song. Valiant Rikki-tikki is dead! For Nagaina will surely kill him underground."

So he sang a very mournful song that he made up on the spur of the minute, and just as he got to the most touching part the grass quivered again, and Rikki-tikki, covered with dirt, dragged himself out of the hole leg by leg, licking his whiskers. Darzee stopped with a little shout. Rikki-tikki shook some of the dust out of his fur and sneezed. "It is all over," he said. "The widow will never come out again." And the red ants that live between the grass stems heard him, and began to troop down one after the other to see if he had spoken the truth.

Rikki-tikki curled himself up in the grass and slept where he was—slept and slept till it was late in the afternoon, for he had done a hard day's work.

"Now," he said, when he awoke, "I will go back to the house. Tell the Coppersmith, Darzee, and he will tell the garden that Nagaina is dead."

The Coppersmith is a bird who makes a noise exactly like the beating of a little hammer on a copper pot; and the reason he is always making it is because he is the town crier to every Indian garden, and tells all the news to everybody who cares to listen. As Rikki-tikki went up the path, he heard his "attention" notes like a tiny dinner gong; and then the steady "*Ding-dong-tock!* Nag is dead—*dong!* Nagaina is dead! *Ding-dong-tock!*"

That set all the birds in the garden singing, and the frogs croaking; for Nag and Nagaina used to eat frogs as well as little birds.

When Rikki got to the house, Teddy and Teddy's mother (she still looked very white, for she had been fainting) and Teddy's father came out and almost cried over him; and that

night he ate all that was given him till he could eat no more, and went to bed on Teddy's shoulder, where Teddy's mother saw him when she came to look late at night.

"He saved our lives and Teddy's life," she said to her husband. "Just think he saved all our lives!"

Rikki-tikki woke up with a jump, for all the mongooses are light sleepers.

"Oh, it's you," said he. "What are you bothering for? All the cobras are dead; and if they weren't, I'm here."

Rikki-tikki had a right to be proud of himself; but he did not grow too proud, and he kept that garden as a mongoose should keep it, with tooth and jump and spring and bite, till never a cobra dared show its head inside the walls.

DR. ZED'S DAZZLING SCIENCE ACTIVITIES

by Gordon Penrose

Magic Illusion Wheels That Change Color When You Spin Them!

1. Begin by tracing a coffee mug on a piece of cardboard to make a wheel about 7.5 cm in diameter. Cut it out.
2. Find the centre of your wheel by drawing two straight lines exactly the same length across it. Mark the place where the lines cross.
3. Punch two small holes with the point of a pencil about 9 mm either side of the centre point.
4. Decorate both sides of your wheel with one of these patterns. Or make a pattern of your own.
5. Cut a piece of strong string about 1 m long and thread the ends through the two holes. Knot the loose ends.

centre

... If you punch a hole near the edge of your wheel it will also whirrr!

Wow! Those colors certainly change when the wheel goes fast!

That's the illusion! Your mind is tricked into seeing a color or colors that aren't really there!

Spinning your wheels!
Wind your wheel up by twirling it as you would a skipping rope. About 20 times will do. Then pull the string tight and see what happens. By pulling the string tight and slackening it, you can keep your wheel spinning. The faster you do this the faster it will spin.

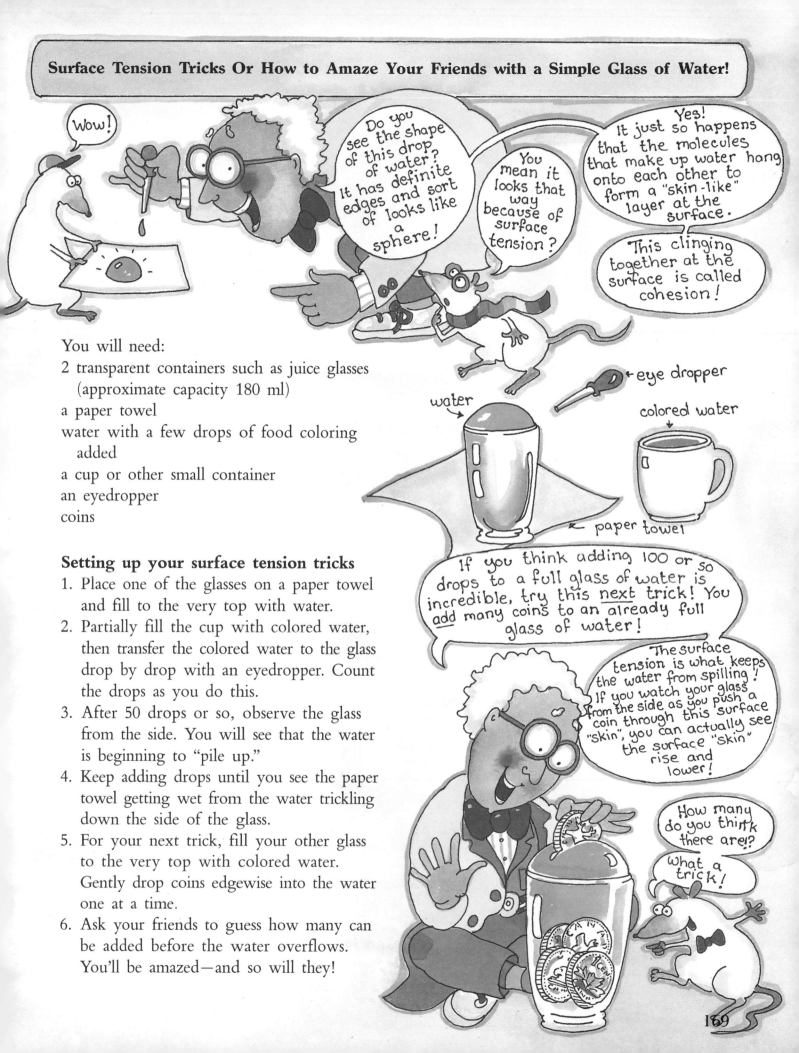

Wow!

Do you see the shape of this drop of water? It has definite edges and sort of looks like a sphere!

You mean it looks that way because of surface tension?

Yes! It just so happens that the molecules that make up water hang onto each other to form a "skin-like" layer at the surface.

This clinging together at the surface is called cohesion!

water ← eye dropper

colored water

← paper towel

You will need:

2 transparent containers such as juice glasses (approximate capacity 180 ml)

a paper towel

water with a few drops of food coloring added

a cup or other small container

an eyedropper

coins

Setting up your surface tension tricks

1. Place one of the glasses on a paper towel and fill to the very top with water.
2. Partially fill the cup with colored water, then transfer the colored water to the glass drop by drop with an eyedropper. Count the drops as you do this.
3. After 50 drops or so, observe the glass from the side. You will see that the water is beginning to "pile up."
4. Keep adding drops until you see the paper towel getting wet from the water trickling down the side of the glass.
5. For your next trick, fill your other glass to the very top with colored water. Gently drop coins edgewise into the water one at a time.
6. Ask your friends to guess how many can be added before the water overflows. You'll be amazed—and so will they!

If you think adding 100 or so drops to a full glass of water is incredible, try this next trick! You add many coins to an already full glass of water!

The surface tension is what keeps the water from spilling! If you watch your glass from the side as you push a coin through this surface "skin", you can actually see the surface "skin" rise and lower!

How many do you think there are!?

What a trick!

The Wildest of All Wild Creatures

by Walter Farley

The next day Alec set out to obtain more of the carragheen. As he neared the rocks, he saw the stallion standing silently beside a huge boulder. Not a muscle twitched in his black body—it was as if an artist had painted the Black on white stone.

Alec climbed down into a small hollow and paused to look out over the rocks below. Suddenly he heard the stallion's scream, more piercing, more blood-curdling than he had ever heard it before. He looked up.

The Black was on his hind legs, his teeth bared. Then with a mighty leap, he shot away from the boulder toward Alec. Swiftly he came—faster with every magnificent stride. He was almost on top of him when he thundered to a halt and reared again. Alec jumped to the side, tripped on a stone, and fell to the ground. High above him the Black's legs pawed the air, and then descended three metres in front of him! Again he went up and down—again and again he pounded. The ground on which Alec lay shook from the force of his hooves. The stallion was frothing at the mouth, and his crazed eyes never left the ground in front of him.

Gradually his pounding lessened and then stopped. He raised his head high and his whistle shrilled through the air. He shook his head and slowly moved away, his nostrils trembling.

Alec regained his feet and cautiously made his way toward the torn earth, his brain flooded with confusion. There in front of him he saw the strewn parts of a long, yellowish-black body, and the diamond-shaped head of a snake, crushed and lifeless. He stood still—the suddenness of discovering life, other than the Black and himself on the island, astounding him! Sweat broke out on his forehead as he realized what a snake bite would have meant—suffering and perhaps death! Dazed, he looked at the stallion just a few metres away. Had the Black killed the snake to save him? Was the stallion beginning to understand that they needed each other to survive?

Slowly the boy walked toward the Black. The stallion's mane swept in the wind, his muscles twitched, his eyes moved restlessly, but he stood his ground as the boy approached. Alec wanted the horse to understand that he would not hurt him. Cautiously he reached a hand toward the stallion's head. The Black drew it back as far as he could without moving. Alec stepped closer and to the side of him. Gently he touched him for an instant. The stallion did not move. Again Alec attempted to touch the savage head. The Black reared and shook a little. Alec said soothingly, "Steady, Black-boy, I wouldn't hurt you." The stallion quivered, then reared again and broke. One hundred metres away he suddenly stopped and turned.

Alec gazed at him, standing there so still—his head raised high in the air. "We'll get out of this somehow, Black—working together," he said determinedly.

Alec walked back to the top of the rocks and again began his descent. He made his way carefully down to the water level. Cautiously he looked before he stepped—where there was one snake there might be more. Reaching the bottom, he once again filled his shirt full of the moss and made his way back. High above him he could see the Black looking out over the cliffs, his mane whipping in the wind. When he reached the top the stallion was still there. He followed a short distance behind as Alec went back to the spring.

Days passed and gradually the friendship between the boy and the Black grew. The stallion now came at his call and let Alec stroke him while he grazed with wondering eyes. One night Alec sat within the warm glow of the fire and watched the stallion munching on the carragheen beside the pool. He wondered if the stallion was as tired of

the carragheen as he. Alec had found that if he boiled it in the turtle shell it formed a gelatinous substance which tasted a little better than the raw moss. A fish was now a rare delicacy to him.

The flame's shadows reached out and cast eerie ghostlike patterns on the Black's body. Alec's eyes glowed and his face became grim as thoughts rushed through his brain. Should he try it tomorrow? Did he dare attempt to ride the Black? Should he wait a few more days? Go ahead—tomorrow. Don't do it! Go ahead—

The fire burned low, then smoldered. Yet

Alec sat beside the fire, his eyes fixed on that blacker-than-night figure beside the spring.

The next morning he woke from a fitful slumber to find the sun high above. Hurriedly he ate some of the carragheen. Then he looked for the Black, but he was not in sight. Alec whistled, but no answer came. He walked toward the hill. The sun blazed down and the sweat rolled from his body. If it would only rain! The last week had been like an oven on the island.

When he reached the top of the hill, he saw the Black at one end of the beach. Again he whistled, and this time there was an answering whistle as the stallion turned his head. Alec walked up the beach toward him, his face resolute.

The Black stood still as he approached. He went cautiously up to him and placed a hand on his neck. "Steady there, boy," he murmured, as the warm flesh quivered slightly beneath his hand. The stallion showed neither fear nor hate of him; his large eyes were still turned on the sea.

For a moment Alec stood with his hand on the Black's neck. Then he walked toward a sand dune a short distance away. The stallion followed. He stepped up the side of the dune, his left hand in the horse's thick mane. The Black's ears pricked forward, his eyes followed the boy nervously—some of the savageness returned to them, his muscles twitched. For a moment Alec was undecided what to do. Then his hands gripped the mane tighter and he threw himself on the Black's back. For a second the stallion stood motionless, then he snorted and plunged; the sand went flying as he doubled in the air. Alec felt the mighty muscles heave, then he was flung through the air, landing heavily on his back. Everything went dark.

Alec regained consciousness to find some-thing warm against his cheek. Slowly he opened his eyes. The stallion was pushing him with his head. Alec tried moving his arms and legs, and found them bruised but not broken. Wearily he got to his feet. The wilderness and savageness had once more disappeared in the Black; he looked as though nothing had happened.

Alec waited for a few minutes—then once again led the stallion to the sand dune. His hand grasped the horse's mane. But this time he only laid the upper part of his body on the stallion's back, while he talked soothingly into his ear. The Black flirted his ears back and forth, as he glanced backward with his black eyes.

"See, I'm not going to hurt you, fella," Alec murmured, as he patted him and let him feel his weight. After a few minutes, Alec cautiously slid on his back. Once again, the stallion snorted and sent the boy flying through the air.

He picked himself up from the ground—slower this time. But when he had rested, he whistled for the Black again. The stallion moved toward him. Alec determinedly stepped on the sand dune and once again let the Black feel his weight. Gently he spoke into a large ear, "It's me, Black-boy, whoa, fella." He slid onto the stallion's back. One arm slipped around his neck as he half-reared. Then like a shot from a gun, the Black broke down the beach. His action shifted, and his huge strides seemed to make him fly through the air.

Alec clung to the stallion's mane for his life. The wind screamed by and he couldn't see! Suddenly the Black swerved and headed up the hill; he reached the top and then down. The spring was a blur as they whipped by. To the rocks he raced, and then the stallion made a wide circle—his speed

never diminishing. Down through a long ravine he rushed. Alec's blurred vision made out a black object in front of them, and as a flash he remembered the deep gully that was there. He felt the stallion gather himself; instinctively he leaned forward and held the Black firm and steady with his hands and knees. Then they were in the air, sailing over the black hole. Alec slid a little when they landed but recovered himself in time to keep from falling off! Once again the stallion reached the beach, his hoof beats regular and rhythmic on the white sand.

The jump had helped greatly in clearing Alec's mind. He leaned closer to the stallion's ear and kept repeating, "Steady, Black-boy, steady." The stallion seemed to glide over the sand and then his speed began to lessen. Alec kept talking to him. Slower and slower ran the Black. Gradually he came to a stop. The boy released his grip from the stallion's mane and his arms encircled the Black's neck. He was weak with exhaustion—he was in no condition for such a ride! Wearily he slipped to the ground. Never had he dreamed a horse could run so fast! The stallion looked at him, his head held high, his large body only slightly covered with sweat.

That night Alec lay wide awake, his body aching with pain, but his heart pounding with excitement. He had ridden the Black!

Acknowledgments

For kind permission to reprint copyrighted material, acknowledgment is hereby made to the following:

Heirs of Bud Abbott and Lou Costello for the routine "Who's on First?" by Abbott and Costello. Copyright ©1978 by Abbott and Costello Enterprises. Used by permission.

The Canadian Speakers and Writers Service Ltd., Ben Wicks and Associates Ltd., and GEMS for selected text and artwork from *Dear World/Cher Monde*. Copyright ©1986 GEMS (Global Ed/Med Supplies). Reprinted by permission.

Jonathan Cape Ltd. for the excerpt from *Chitty Chitty Bang Bang: The Magical Car* by Ian Fleming. Copyright ©1964 by Glidrose Productions Ltd. Reprinted by permission of the publisher.

Cricket Magazine for "Dear Book, I Love You" by Caroline Feller Bauer. Copyright ©1980 by Open Court Publishing Co. Reprinted by permission.

Doubleday & Co., Inc., for the excerpt from *The Neverending Story* by Michael Ende, translated by Ralph Manheim. Copyright ©1983 by Doubleday & Co., Inc. Reprinted by permission of the publisher.

Faber and Faber Limited for the excerpt from *The Iron Man* by Ted Hughes. Copyright ©1968 by Ted Hughes. Reprinted by permission of the publisher.

Mirra Ginsburg for "Three Rolls and One Doughnut" and "How the Peasant Helped His Horse" from *Three Rolls and One Doughnut*. Copyright ©1970 by Mirra Ginsburg. Reprinted by permission of the author.

Greey de Pencier Books for the text of "Magic Illusion Wheels" and "Surface Tension Tricks" from *Doctor Zed's Brilliant Book of Science Experiments* by Gordon Penrose; and for text and photographs from "Granny's Gang" by Katherine McKeever. Copyright ©1984 Greey de Pencier Books, an *OWL* book. Reprinted by permission of the publisher.

Dagmar Guarino for her story "Inside Out." Copyright ©1982 by *Ms* Foundation for Education and Communications, Inc. Reprinted by permission of the author.

Patricia Hancock for her poem "A Family Affair." Copyright ©1979 by Patricia Hancock. Reprinted by permission of the author.

Harper & Row, Publishers, Inc., for entire text of *The Girl Who Loved the Wind* by Jane Yolen (Thomas Y. Crowell Company). Copyright ©1972 Berne Convention; for the adaptation of "i am the running girl" by Arnold Adoff. Copyright ©1979 by Arnold Adoff; and for the text and illustrations of "The Snow in Chelm" from *Zlateh the Goat and Other Stories* by Isaac Bashevis Singer. Copyright ©1966 by Isaac Bashevis Singer. Illustrations by Maurice Sendak. All reprinted by permission of Harper & Row, Publishers, Inc.

Henry Holt & Co., Inc., for the excerpt from *Time Cat, The Remarkable Journeys of Jason and Gareth* by Lloyd Alexander. Copyright ©1963 by Lloyd Alexander. Reprinted by permission of the publisher.

Houghton Mifflin Company for text and illustration (page 214 and Plate 55) from *A Field Guide to the Birds* by Roger Tory Peterson. Copyright 1934, 1938, and 1947 by Roger Tory Peterson. Copyright © renewed 1974 by Roger Tory Peterson. Reprinted by permission of Houghton Mifflin Company.

Irwin Publishing Inc. for the excerpt from *The Boy Who Came with Cartier* by Chip Young. Copyright © 1974 by Clarke, Irwin & Company Limited. Reprinted by permission of Irwin Publishing Inc.

Tot Jones for her story "The Captive." Copyright © 1983 by Tot Jones.

First published in *Cricket* Magazine, November 1983. Reprinted by permission of the author.

Little, Brown and Company for "How to Become a Magician," "Penny on the Nose," and "The Fool Me, Fool You Trick" from *Mr. Mysterious's Secrets of Magic* by Sid Fleischman. Copyright ©1975 by Sid Fleischman, Inc. Reprinted by permission of the publisher.

Macmillan Publishing Co. for the poem "Today Is Saturday" from *Today Is Saturday* by Zilpha Keatley Snyder. Copyright ©1969 by Zilpha Keatley Snyder; and for the poem "From Sandia Mountain to Sky Pueblo" from *A God on Every Mountain Top* by Byrd Baylor. Copyright ©1981 by Byrd Baylor. Both reprinted by permission of Atheneum Publishers, A Division of Macmillan, Inc.

The Canadian Publishers, McClelland and Stewart Limited, for the excerpt from *The Secret World of Og* by Pierre Berton. Copyright ©1961 by Pierre Berton; and for the excerpt from *The House at Pooh Corner* by A.A. Milne. Copyright ©1956 by A.A. Milne. Both reprinted by permission of the publisher.

Methuen Children's Books for the illustrations of "The Dodo" and "The Passenger Pigeon" from *As Dead As a Dodo* by Shawn Rice. Copyright ©1981 by Shawn Rice. Reprinted by permission of Associated Book Publishers (UK) Ltd.

William Morrow & Co., Inc., for excerpted text and illustrations from *Chapter 4 of Ramona and Her Father* by Beverly Cleary. Illustrations by Alan Tiegreen. Copyright ©1975, 1977 by Beverly Cleary. Reprinted by permission of the publisher.

Lyrics for "Tears Are Not Enough" by David Foster, Brian Adams, and Jim Vallance. Copyright ©1985 Northern Lights for Africa Society. Reprinted by permission of Northern Lights for Africa Society.

Oxford University Press Canada for the poem "Today and Yesterday" by Robert Heidbreder from *Don't Eat Spiders* by Robert Heidbreder. Copyright ©1985 by Robert Heidbreder; and for "Nanabozho and the Wild Geese" from *Tales of Nanabozho* by Dorothy M. Reid. Copyright ©1963 Oxford University Press Canada. Both reprinted by permission of the publisher.

Penguin Books Ltd. for the excerpt from *Colin's Fantastic Video Adventure* by Kenneth Oppel (Puffin Books, 1985). Copyright ©Kenneth Oppel, 1985. Reprinted by permission of the publisher.

Nancy Prasad for her haiku poems "A Sudden Gust of Wind," which appeared in CICADA (1981), and "Fragment of Sky." Reprinted by permission of the author.

Random House, Inc., for the poem "Together" from *Embrace: Selected Love Poems* by Paul Engle. Copyright ©1969 by Paul Engle; and for the excerpt from "The Wildest of All Wild Creatures" from *The Black Stallion* by Walter Farley. Copyright 1941 and copyright renewed ©1969 by Walter Farley. Reprinted by permission of International Creative Management for Walter Farley and Random House, Inc.

Raymond Rohauer for photographs from *The Goat* (1921) Metro Pictures Corp., and from *The Best of Buster*. Copyright ©1976 Darien House, Inc. Copyrights assigned to Raymond Rohauer. All rights reserved. Reprinted by permission.

Scholastic-TAB Publications Ltd. for the excerpts from *That Scatterbrain Booky*, copyright ©1981 by Bernice Thurman Hunter; and from *Margaret In the Middle*, copyright ©1986 by Bernice Thurman Hunter. Both reprinted by permission of the publisher.

Ian Serraillier for "The Greedy Butchers" from *Robin in the Greenwood*, retold by Ian Serraillier. Copyright ©1967 by Ian Serraillier. Reprinted by permission.

Illustrations

Steve Beinicke, 148–149; Ron Burg, 24–27, 66–71; Harvey Chan, 89–92; David Chang, 116; Brenda Clarke, 77–78; Joanne Coulton, 151–155; Holly Dean, 44; John Fraser, 102–104; Carlos Freire, 79–82; Katherine Helmer, 72–74, 139–141; Tina Holdcroft, 168–169; Rob Johanssen, 134–136; Kristin Kan, 18 (bottom right); Nancy Kettles, 6–7; Barbara Klunder, 20–22; Jock MacRae, 54–57; 170–174; Alli Marshall, 18 (top left); Sharon Matthews, 124–128; Peter Moffman, 96 (top right, bottom); Linda Montgomery, 110–112; San Murata, 156–167; Karen Patkau, 60–61; Maureen Paxton, 40–43; Roger Tory Peterson, 47; Shawn Rice, 58–59; Tasha Riley, 19; Maurice Sendak, 29–30; Martin Springett, 62; Ray Taylor, 129–132; Tom Taylor, 98–101; Alan Tiegreen, 14–16; Henry Vanderlinde, 28; Vlasta Van Kampen, 46–49; Graeme Walker, 75–76; Sue Wilkinson, 117–119.

Photographs:

Mark E. Alsop, 95 (right); Canadian National Exhibition Archives, 150; Ian Crysler, 146–147, 148–170 (book covers); City of Toronto Archives, 31 (background); Andreas Dannenberg/*Time* Magazine, 94, 97 (bottom); Four by Five Inc., 107 (top left, bottom left and right), 108 (top and middle inclusive), 109; German Archaeological Institute/Focus, 133, 136 (top), 137; Jeremy Jones, 17; Carolyn Meland, 8–10; Metro Pictures Corporation (Buster Keaton, author) LP16562, copyright renewed ©Raymond Rohauer, 34–39; Masterfile, 144; Miller Services, 96 (right); Mitsubishi Electric Corp., 95 (middle); Michel Mateo Murphy, 120, 121 (insert); Nintendo of America Inc., 95 (left); Owl Rehabilitation Foundation, 52–53; Danny Pelchat, 121, 122; *Robotics Today*, Dec. 1985, published by Society of Manufacturing Engineers, 95 (top right); Dimo Safari, 142–143; Liam Sharp, 86, 88; K.A. Stockton /Cybermation, Inc., 96 (left); *Technology Illustrated*, June 1983, 97 (top); Anthony Thomas Photography, 2, 11–13, 31 (inset)–33; 64–65, 106, 107 (top right), 108 (middle left), 113–115, 176; *The Toronto Star*, 84–85; Helena Wilson, 50.